ROMANY RETURNS

Guy Loveridge

For Douglas Loveridge
and Richard Burns - you showed me how.

For Mum Dad and Ma
You're still showing me.

Cover Artwork by Emma S.J.Taylor B.A. From an original by Guy Loveridge.

Printed in the UK on behalf of Richard Netherwood Limited

Published by Douglas Loveridge Publications

ISBN 1 900113 00 7

BIOGRAPHY

This is Guy Loveridge's first book. It has taken him nearly five years, but this has not put him off, however, and he is already working on his second.

Guy was educated at Berkhampstead School where he played 3rd XI Cricket, Captained the Shooting Team and debated. He left there in 1988 from where he went around the world, visiting New Zealand, Australia, The United States and much of Europe.

1989 found Guy in Huddersfield embarking upon a degree course. This he succesfully graduated from in 1993 with a B.A. (Honours). On the way he flew with the Battle of Britain Memorial Flight in the 50th Anniversary Season. He maintains an interest in aviation and holds a current R.A.C. Racing Licence.

Romany Watt with Mr. & Mrs. Terry Waite, Romany's Vardo in Wilmslow - 1993

FOREWORDS

I welcome this tribute to my father, known to millions of children and adults in the thirties and forties as "Romany of the B.B.C. Children's Hour". The author, Guy Loveridge, has caught the warmth of his broadcasts and books. I find this especially touching as he died twenty six years before Guy was born.

I hope this book will make more people more aware of the beauty and fragility of the countryside, and I thank him very much for having written it.

Romany Watt.
Oxford. 1995.

Some of the most treasured books in my library are the books written by G. Bramwell Evens, better known as Romany of the B.B.C. they are before me as I write. "Out with Romany", "Romany, Murial and Doris", "A Romany and Raq", the list goes on.

Romany introduced thousands of children of my generation to the wonders of the countryside. Together with his faithfull Springer Spaniel 'Raq' he travelled throughout the North of England and kept me enthralled. Although during the war years all B.B.C. programmes were scripted, Romany managed to convey such a sense of reality that it came as a great shock to learn that all his programmes were recorded in the studio. He often deviated from the script and kept his companions, Murial, Doris and others on their toes.

He was a prolific writer but regrettably, the Romany books, treasured by children of the forties, are out of print. Now Guy Loveridge has put matters right and brought together this selection from his writings. The "William" books by Richmal Crompton are of roughly the same vintage and have recently enjoyed a remarkable revival. It would not surprise me if "Romany Returns" did equally well.

Romany has given me a lifetime of good memories. This book will revive the past for many and will also introduce a whole new generation to the joys of the countryside.

Terry Waite.
Suffolk. 1995.

CONTENTS

BACKGROUND NOTE

The Reverend George Bramwell Evens broadcast on the B.B.C. Children's Hour for over ten years, first on the Northern B.B.C., but then from 1932 on the national "Home Service". The impact of the things that happened in those programmes is very hard to appreciate now, fifty years after Romany's death. I would implore the reader of this book to find a friend or relative over the age of, say fifty seven. If they listened to Children's Hour during the last war then they will know Romany. Ask them what they thought about the man that they listened to every Tuesday evening before Mummy and Daddy tuned into the News. Ask them about the excursions into the countryside that flooded into so many suburban parlours for the twenty five or thirty minutes before the stark realities of the World at War encroached once again into their young lives. You will be surprised at the vivid nature of their re- collections and the warmth of feeling that they still hold, perhaps unstirred by conscious thought since childhood for this man. Then you will realise why I decided to write this book.

I am 25 and so, obviously, never heard Romany broadcast. I was given one of his books, "Out with Romany Again", by my father when I was nine years old. He had listened to Romany and was, I think, trying to instil the same love for, and awareness of, the countryside that he had been given. He succeeded, but I am certain that he never thought that fifteen years later I would be preparing a book to serve a dual purpose: to commemorate the Fiftieth Anniversary of the death of a man who touched the lives of literally millions in the most gentle of ways, and to illustrate that there was a man in the 1920-40's who was thinking clearly and intelligently about the dangers that the countryside faced and the consequences of not heeding the balance that, until this century, had always existed between man and nature. I hope that the people who knew and loved Romany as both a broadcaster and a preacher will find something here that will remind them of him. And to those who did not know him then perhaps this will steer you to his books or even to look at the birds and the hedges around you in a new way.

At this point I must thank the many people who have been invaluable in the preparation of this book. There are too many of you to name individually, such is Romany's legacy, but special heart felt thanks must go to Romany Watt, Romany's daughter who lives today in Oxford. Her warmth and enthusiasm for the project and her welcome to a twenty something stranger with an arm full of notes, a tape recorder and a Frog Eyed Sprite was fantastic. My warmest thanks and love go to her and her large family. Thanks also to Victoria: you restored what I thought was broken forever.

In her biography of her husband Eunice Evens says:

"I am sitting in my bedroom window at Old Parks as I write, and in my utter incapacity to describe the scene of surpassing loveliness before me makes me wonder if I should have ever attempted to write this book."

In these words I can find both understanding and fellow feeling. I recently spent a few days in the Lake District and spoke to people who remember Romany and read the recollections of many more. On this visit I also went to Old Parks Farm for the first time. On the drive from Keswick, the closer that the car came to Glassonby the more I was aware of the 'Spirit of Romany'. In that countryside one can imagine turning a corner to be greeted with the sight of a Romany vardo pulled at a steady pace by a horse called Comma and exchanging a cheery word with the man sitting on the step with his playful looking spaniel beside him.

When we reached the farm and walked through the fields that roll down to the beck and across to the splendid hills beyond I saw the bird-bath that was erected to mark the scattering of Romany's ashes. The positioning could not be better. All around I could see and hear the sights and sounds that he loved and held so dear. I still feel humbled by the place and the thoughts that it evoked. I questioned why I was writing this book and if I really had any business to do so. In the end, after much soul searching and thought, I have decided that there is no way that I can do the memory of Romany the service that it deserves by trying to re-write his biography: that job has already been done so very well by Eunice Evens in her book "Through the Years with Romany". Instead of that I am simply going to try to show that the memory of Romany is still strong, to select my own favourites from among his stories, to list the books he wrote and just mentioned the outline of the events in his life. In these pages I trust that I commit no act that disparages anyone's memories. I hope that I can, in fact, enhance something and allow it to come again to life.

Inevitably I can not convey what it was like to listen to Romany or to have read his books at a time when there was always the tantalising hope that one might meet the man himself and ruffle Raq's fur. I hope, however, that the people who have given their time to this project in their memories, give you, my reader, the chance to see what it was like to go "Out with Romany" or how one felt to be sitting in a church listening to one of his sermons. If Romany is outside your generation, as he is mine, then I hope that you can find here in his writing something of the magic that made him such a loved man in his own day, and perhaps something may be there as well that says something about the way life used to be lived and give us a clue to what went wrong? Or at the very least, show us how we have all changed.

Guy Loveridge.
Huddersfield. Spring 1995.

"THIS IS THE B.B.C. HOME SERVICE...."

George Bramwell Evens was born in Hull in April 1884. His mother and father were in Hull running the Salvation Army Mission. His mother was of traditional Romani stock and the family already had a celebrity as his Uncle Rodney was the famous evangelist and preacher, Gypsy Smith. Bram was destined to spend the first seven years of his life in a far from normal environment as his parents soon severed the connection with the Salvation Army and the stability that it provided and chose instead to tour the country giving ten day "residences" in various towns. And thus to preach and bring the word of God to far larger numbers of people than they would have done in Hull. Bram took an increasingly prominent part in their services after his first appearance at a prayer meeting at the age of four. There he sang and, because of his beautiful voice, he continued to sing at all their meetings. He was very proud to have his own songs specially noted in his mother's song book. This way of life continued until the family settled in Liverpool when his father was appointed as the minister of a Wesleyan Church there. Then he began to lead a life that bore more resemblance to what could be called "normal". It was here that he came into contact with Polly Furzland. She was a Cornish girl that they had met on one of their missions and whom they had "converted". She came to the manse in Liverpool to be the family maid. She was a long and loyal friend and Bram always spoke of her with kindness and fun. He pretended to blame her for his untidiness as an adult, suggesting that she was too conscientious in her work and thus did not chide him for leaving his things in a mess! It was at this early age that Bram learnt of people's irrational intolerance of "indifferences": where he had previously taken great pride in his Romani heritage, he was shocked and puzzled to find that such hatred and derision could be put into the word "Gypsy". These were experiences that he never forgot and perhaps they helped instil in him the tolerance and honesty that so characterised his adult life.

Despite his natural enthusiasm and interest in the world around him, Bram was not the most accomplished scholar. So at the age of thirteen his parents decided to send him away to boarding school. This was to prove to be the start of the happiest days of his life, but quite naturally at the time he welcomed the prospect with something less than enthusiasm! It was whilst he was at Epworth College that he formulated the ideas that would lead him into the ministry and the life that brought him into contact with so many people. It was the benevolent and, one could say loving head -mastership of J. C. Beattie that encouraged him to grow both as a man and spiritually. Mr. Beattie encouraged the young Bram to discover for himself the wonders of both the scriptures and of the natural world around him. And so when the time came for him to leave he was clear in his decision to enter the Wesleyan Ministry. Although it was also his parents' avowed career choice for him, it was a decision that he made for himself and one that he never regreted. He was able to find a balance the highly public life that he was to lead in the last dozen years of his life and the quiet spirituality that he would have preferred through his faith and conviction. He believed that what he was doing was what the Lord wanted and something that would bring more people to a greater understanding of the world in which they lived , and God's part in it.

From the fatherly headmaster ship of Mr. Beattie, Bram moved on to Queen's College in Taunton, Somerset. He entered college as a divinity student with an annual Scholarship of thirty pounds towards his tuition. Despite not seeing eye to eye with his new principal, Bram was happy enough as he was able to play as much sport as he wanted and also wandered freely around the lanes of Devon and Somerset. It was whilst at Queens that he actually began to preach, and whilst no record of those early sermons exists it would be interesting to know if they showed the foundations of the style that would hold so many congregations transfixed in later years.

When he left school Bram was still too young to enter the Clergy and so, as a candidate for the Wesleyan Ministry he had to spend a year off doing probationary church work, and was sent to Colchester in Essex. He was the first minister in a brand new church and took great pride in this, and the fact that he could afford to live very comfortably on the ninety pounds a year stipend that he was earning.

Bram always remembered the year of Colchester as a happy one, and indeed the mother of one family that he befriended was always called "Other-mother" when he wrote or referred to her.

After the pleasure of his first "real" job Bram was expectantly looking forward to entering Divinity College. However a harsh blow came when he failed the medical on account of a strange heart abnormality. Bram argued stridently that he had led such an active and sporting life that this must surely have no real bearing. After having consulted a heart specialist he won his argument and was assured that he could look forward to a normal life with no ill effects. After winning his battle Bram was sent to the Wesleyan Theological College in Handsworth on the outskirts of Birmingham. Here he excelled in games and continued his position from school as Captain of Soccer. Because of his height, which was already past six foot, he was unanimously elected goalkeeper. Despite the rather restrictive nature of college life, Bram could not have been in a better location and was to spend much of his spare time roaming the West Midland countryside. During his time at Handsworth, Bram felt himself moved to distance himself from his parents', style of "missionary" preaching and to rather regret the idea of "playing on" his Gypsy ancestry to get an audience. He was no less proud of his background, but simply felt that the more conventional life of a Methodist Minister would suit him better than the Evangelistic Meetings of his earlier life. This was the first time that he has consciously questioned his parents and any potential rift was avoided by him spending very little time at home. After his three years at Handsworth, and despite any lingering doubts he may have had about the exact nature of his calling, Bram was ordained at the Wesleyan Methodist Conference that was held in Cardiff in July of 1908.

Bram's first parish was far from what he would have chosen himself. Instead of some country parish he was sent to Dalston in the East End of London. Here he was not satisfied with the accommodation assigned him and so searched for a week for something that he really liked. The next most important task was to find a dog. His previous years at college were the only time in his life that he went without the companionship of a dog. Soon a terrier, called Jack, arrived home with his new master.

Despite the rather unprepossessing nature of his would-be constituents, Bram soon managed to build both a reputation and a large congregation. He tried to combine his church activities with concerts and plays. So his church became a meeting place for the secular and the spiritual . He also tried to get out to Epping Forest as often as he could. This was the nearest piece of "real" countryside. London Fields and Hackney Downs were much closer but they did not qualify!

One Saturday in late 1910 Bram invited a young Guildhall School of Music student to perform in his Church. After the performance he captivated the young lady and the very next day, asked her to join his proposed "Costume Concert Party". She modestly agreed, and when he learnt that he was to move on to a new mission in Yorkshire he asked her to be his wife. This young lady was, of course, Eunice Thomas, and they were married by her father on the first of August 1911 in Dalston Congregational Church. The couple honeymooned in Wales at the home of Bram's beloved Polly, his childhood friend.

After the industrial surroundings of Dalston the newlyweds were hoping for a more rural and picturesque home in Yorkshire. Unfortunately the moors and dales that they had both imagined were nowhere to be seen in the drab surrounds of Goole. They were disappointed by the manse. The accommodation provided by the church fell a little below what they both felt was suitable. But with Bram's artistic eye and the sterling help of a maid that Bram had engaged from London, they soon removed evidence of previous generations of incumbents and felt able to welcome visitors. Another regret in leaving the south was that he was unable to continue at first hand the friendship that had grown between him and the artist Gregory Brown. He was then becoming well known for his paintings that appeared as posters promoting the London Underground. Bram often accompanied Gregory on sketching trips and although he lacked the patience to prepare his work adequately he did manage to produce some attractive water-colours that conveyed his love of the country. It may be the lessons that he learnt here were of use to him later as he was able to illustrate his nature talks with lightening sketches in charcoal.

A great relief to the Evens's was that they could bicycle to the outlying villages around Goole. This gave them the chance to see some more pleasant countryside and to meet their more rural flock. It was here that Bram excelled, as he was able to talk to the farmers in their own language without appearing to condescend. He would discuss the price of beef and the health of the herd in ways that brought him instant friends. It was perhaps this need to be "out and about" coupled with his natural dislike of officialdom that led him into direct conflict with his church elders. It was the arrival of their first child, Glyn that may have led him to fail the final part of his degree in the Summer of 1912. This seems to have been of more a disappointment to his wife than it ever was to him. Just as the young family were settling down, it was decided to move him on again. September 1914 is remembered for very sad and dark reasons world-wide. For the Evens family it was equally momentous as they saw the Cumberland Fells for the first time and started a new life in Carlisle.

Eunice Evens remembered the family's arrival in Carlisle for two main reasons: firstly, Glyn misbehaved so badly on arrival at the manse, that he had to have his tea by himself in the kitchen. Secondly, as soon as the welcoming group of new parishioners had departed, Bram disappeared out of the back of the house and spent the remaining hours until dark exploring the countryside. Eunice could have been forgiven for being very annoyed at being left alone with all the luggage and baggage from the move to sort out, but when Bram returned the look of sheer pleasure on his face and the tales he had of the river and of the things he had seen made sure that she forgave him.

As he was of military age Bram felt that he should enlist and so he joined the volunteers for Kitchener's Army. He was amazed that the same heart murmur that nearly precluded him from the ministry also rendered him unfit for duty. It is, with the benefit of hindsight, perhaps a blessing that he did not go, as many of his fellow 1914 volunteers were killed at the Battle of Mons. Surely his comfort and work during two World Wars and the intervening years more than made up for his inability to serve.

The little town of Carlisle was in for a rude shock. Its population ballooned almost overnight as thousands of munitions workers flooded into the town. Despite the potential for huge attendances at services it seemed to be the public houses rather than the local churches that gained the benefit of their patronage. To attempt to rectify this situation Bram approached the authorities and asked permission to rent a cinema on a Sunday evening to try to appeal to a wider cross section of people. He was allowed to do so and the evening was advertised widely. On the appointed date he and Eunice arrived early and were disappointed to find only a couple of hundred people waiting outside and the cinemas lights extinguished. When he went up to the box office and asked why the frontage was not illuminated, he was stunned to be told by the manager that the cinema was already full to capacity. He had turned off the lights to dissuade any more people! The services held in the cinema remained capacity affairs for the next six years and continued until 1920.

Having become a friend to the munitions workers Bram decided that there should be a purpose build place for them to meet during the week and in which he could hold Sunday services. He managed to persuade the authorities to have a club built in the munitions factory site. That he achieved this must have been due to his forceful personality and his success with the cinema meetings. The only snag was that he had to undertake the job of Supervisor. This necessitated him buying a car to travel to the factory. He spent twenty pounds on his purchase and, having been shown all the pedals, levers and switches by the garage owner, he drove it straight home. Lessons, and indeed a test, were not compulsory in those days and his progress as a self taught driver was not without mis-hap. Nor was his choice, a Trumball, the most reliable. So he spent much of his time walking back from his abandoned car! He also decided that he had to be on the spot. So Eunice, Glyn and Bram moved into the club shell just as the winter snows arrived. They lived for some months in the one completed room and put up with five foot snowdrifts and the absence of glass in the windows. His diligence soon paid off, however, when the workers began to join him at the end of their shifts to help with the finishing of "their club".

Bram's efforts were recognised in higher places as well. He was invited to meet the King and Queen when they came to view the munitions factory. He was so busy that he did not see the need to go back into Carlisle for his best suit. In the end Eunice persuaded him, although he still managed to meet the Royal Party in plaster covered shoes! The hard work and hardships that the family put up with during this period were repaid handsomely when they were invited to stay on in Carlisle. This meant that Bram would be able to build upon the good relationships that he had already forged.

Almost immediately, however, he faced a seemingly insurmountable problem: the Methodist Church in Carlisle was declared unsafe on account of wood-worm so they had to begin looking for ways to raise money for a new building. They received a huge boost when Joseph Rank, a well known millionaire baker and Methodist Philanthropist offered them a cheque for ten thousand pounds. The only problem was that he stipulated that this should be used to build a "hall" rather than a church. For a time this stymied Bram until he worked with an architect called H. E. Ayris and produced a design for the new hall that captured all the splendour of a church. The design was accepted and all minds turned to raising the outstanding sixteen thousand pounds that it would cost to build. Many events and bazaars, jumble sales and the like were held until the day for the opening arrived and the project was only one thousand pounds in debt. Huge crowds came to the opening, which was to be chaired by Mister Rank himself.

Bram and Eunice's daughter, Romany June, takes up the story:

"Rank, who was on the platform, had promised to double the day's collection, when Bram suddenly asked if he could add the month's subscriptions to the plate. When Rank nodded, it brought the house down, and the target was reached: the Hall was opened free of debt!"

Having achieved so much for them it was appropriate for the church authorities to allow Bram more freedom in the running of "his" church. In 1925 he and Eunice started a series of Celebrity Lectures in the Central Hall. These attracted many notable figures, including Sir Walford Davies, who congratulated Bram before his lecture on having: "a beautiful hall which is a church, and a beautiful church that is a hall." If one travels to the Central Hall in Fisher Street today, as I did, one can be assured of a warm and friendly welcome. Sitting in the hall there is a great sense of peace and calm. The decor is much as Bram planned, the large seat for the minister with carvings of flowers and animals on it being the same one that he had made. There is something about the place that feels human and natural, a great achievement for a man in the 1920's to instil such feelings into a building that it truly became the "House of God."

There is a simple tablet on the wall of the entrance hall which says "During the ministry of the Rev. G. Bramwell Evens, 1914-1926, this Hall was built." It was erected after the family had left Carlisle and was done without their knowledge.

The years in Carlisle were probably the most important in Bram's life. It was the first time that he had had the backing of his elders to develop a parish as he wished. It was also in Carlisle that he began to write and lecture about his love of the countryside. He was invited to close the first session of lectures himself and was so successful that Eunice questioned whether he had not missed his true calling in life. She could not have dreamed what the future held.

The years in Carlisle brought three important new arrivals to the Evens household. In 1924 they welcomed a bouncing baby girl, and christened her Romany June. They bought a new dog, a cocker spaniel called Raq. He and his successor Ruin, and a couple of later dogs called Raq, were to be famous in Bram's books and broadcasts. Their final investment was not alive, but had no less an impact on the family. In 1921 they bought a genuine Romany Vardo at Brough Hill Fair. Bram was thrilled with his brightly painted purchase. Eunice was not quite so sure. But once again Bram's vivid imagination could see its potential.

He had been searching for a vardo for some time, but wanted a horse drawn wagon like those of his forefathers. He bought it from the Lovell family after long negotiations. They then hired a horse and christened it Comma. "Because it never came to a full stop", and drove it into the yard at the Fisher Street manse.

Bram then set to work to strip the interior and rebuild it as a fully self sufficient travelling base. He fashioned a folding table and seats that doubled as beds. He divided the area into cooking and living areas and added a roof ventilator and put in an extra window. They were so keen to get it finished that they worked through a heat wave scraping off the gaudy old paint outside and in and splashing on a quieter dark green and white. They finally donned swim suits, overalls and sandals to felt and tar the roof. Eunice says "The tar ran everywhere except where it was meant to go, and we spent half our time unsticking ourselves and our shoes from the roof".

They had already decided on a site and, pulled by Comma, the vardo was taken to Harelow Mill on the river at Cannonbie. It was in the vardo that Bram found inspiration for his writing. He was already contributing articles to the Methodist Recorder and The Cumberland News under the pseudonym of The Tramp. These early pieces differ from later work as he tried to capture the full flavour of local characters, and much of the conversation is in dialect. He dropped this later. I think the readers of his later books were more interested in the sights and sounds of the natural world than the opinions of farmers and village folk. Eventually, he either ignored people completely, or just used them to get himself into special situations. Muriel and Dorris were very important to the B.B.C. programme, but for him, it was a device to make nature more accessible. You could hardly have had a programme in which a man talked to himself and his dog ! With their questions and exclamations, Muriel and Doris brought a wonderfully informal air and children hardly realised that they were learning.

In my research, I found that everyone remembered Muriel and Doris and many recalled Raq and Comma. But only a few remembered Tim Fletcher, the farmer's son and John Rubb the angler. I think the immense popularity of the later broadcasts wiped out earlier memories. It was estimated that thirteen million tuned into "Out with Romany" on those Tuesday evenings... nine million children and four million adults ... !

Thousands more read the books. By 1958, 58,000 people had bought the first "A Romany in the Fields". In all he wrote ten books, plus four written by his son Glyn. The listeners' interest was fuelled by the fact that they already knew the background and had met a number of the characters who were featured on the wireless. There is no question that the broadcasts had the greater impact.

After the great success in Carlisle the family were moved to the industrial Yorkshire town of Huddersfield. The Methodist Church seems to work on the principle that a minister should move around the country, especially if he has made a great success in one particular area, so that his talents are distributed throughout the Wesleyan Movement, and thus strengthen the whole church. Despite accepting this, one can forgive the family being a little depressed as they approached Huddersfield. Having left the rolling hills and woods of Lakeland the moors around Huddersfield must have seemed very bleak and inhospitable. Although they were used to intensive industry with the munitions factories around the Carlisle and Gretna area nothing could have prepared them for the harsh skyline of factories and chimneys around their new home. Although, as Eunice says, they did approach the town from "its more sordid side", it can not have held attraction. It was fortunate that the manse was so near Huddersfield's Greenhead Park. This is a splendidly landscaped Victorian park that is dominated by a huge colonnaded memorial to the dead of both World Wars.

The chapel in Huddersfield no longer exists, although the road in which it stood has been re-named "Chapel Hill". This church was just outside the town centre and in the shadow of the Sellars engineering factory. Bram's responsibilities included preaching on the local circuit, and it was perhaps on these tours of the country area that he found his greatest happiness during their three year stay in Fitzwilliam Street. It was during his years in Huddersfield that Bram found his greatest soulmate. In Rennie Woods, a weaver from Nelson in Lancashire, Bram discovered a great friend and someone to teach him more about photographing wild life. I feel that Eunice sometimes despaired a little of her husband's sanity in the lengths that he would go to in order to get the exact picture that he wanted. It is famously recounted how he climbed to the top of a church steeple in Manchester Road Huddersfield in order to capture a good shot of a rook's nest when a sudden gust of wind nearly pitched him the eighty feet down into the grave yard below! I think that the most important thing that happened during Bram's short stay in Huddersfield was that he was asked by Ernest Woodhead to write a weekly nature column for the Huddersfield Examiner. These columns appeared every Saturday under the title "The Lure of the Open Air". He did not want to write under his own name, perhaps keeping in mind the disapproval from church members over his outside activities in his earlier parishes, and so he took the name of 'The Tramp' again. These columns were so well received that they had centre page top positioning with a pen and ink illustration. All around Huddersfield there are people today who remember the tall, quiet man who came to preach one Sunday out of every month and then ate with a local family. It must have been his love of real people and dislike of any kind of stuffiness that endeared him to the bluff, hard working people of the grimy, industrial West Riding. Bram's favourite place in Huddersfield was the vast park land at West Bretton. This is now a college of higher education and the home of the Yorkshire Sculpture Park. Walking there today one can see the beauty and peace that attracted him.

After only three years in Huddersfield Bram's duodenal trouble, first diagnosed in their final days in Carlisle, again became a problem. It was a very hard job in the Buxton Road chapel, compounded by his having to travel to out-lying villages so frequently. Eunice and Bram discussed the idea of his leaving the ministry, and would have done so if the offer of a church with a much lighter work load had not come up. The huge attraction of this church was that, apart from giving them a home and maintaining his three hundred and twenty pound salary, it was less than ten miles away: just across the hill in Halifax. So the family moved into the manse at King Cross. This was next to the church itself and had the graveyard for its garden. It was also in the shadow of the Wainhouse Folly. This is a vast column which dominates the skyline of the valley. It was build in the late nineteenth century out of spite by a builder who wanted to be able to overlook his neighbours, no matter how high a fence they might erect.

The cost of the tower was forty thousand pounds. Upon the death of Mr. Wainhouse it was sold to the corporation of Halifax for four hundred pounds. While it remains today the manse has gone. It, in fact became uninhabitable during the Evens ministry. They were bought a new house in Rothwell Road. Here Bram was able to expand and plant a garden. It also had a small paddock and a number of outhouses and here he kept an aviary of budgies. Although he may have missed the folly because of the refuge it gave to passing birds of prey, Eunice was more then relieved to move. Partly because she feared for her and baby June's life every time the wind blew, and partly because she was the first tenant of the new manse.

Bram also took an active interest in the Scout group that was attached to his church. Eunice notes with a sadness tinged with pride that of the Scouts that he had taken to camp at Luddenden Dean: "Of the fifty today serving with the forces, unfortunately, eight of those whom my husband knew have already lost their lives."

During the next ten years in Halifax he was encouraged by both his wife and his doctor to take more leisure time. To this end the vardo was moved to a Yorkshire site in an orchard on the river bank at Sleights. It was then moved to Eskdalesdie after winter flooding. On the road from Sleights to Grosmont you will still find a row of cottages called Hardstruggle, which was his address for the summer months. The new site was in a field next to a fine wood with the River Esk sparkling in the valley below. The site was idyllic and would subsequently play a major part in the B.B.C. scripts.

To help his health even further Bram was encouraged to purchase a beach hut at Sandsend near Whitby. It was typical of him that he only agreed after seeking out the one that was furthest from the others and so afforded the greatest opportunities for uninterrupted nature study. The widening of his scope of activities in Halifax culminated in his first programme on the Northern B.B.C. It was in 1931 that he began twelve years of the programmes that would bring him such fame and celebrity. In her biography of him Eunice expresses a little regret that her husband became 'public property' for the last dozen years of his life. His daughter Romany June says much the same thing today. One feels that it was not a question of resentment, but more that he as a father suddenly became just as important to several hundreds of thousands, and eventually millions, of other children. All of them complete strangers, and yet all of them with the feeling that they had a claim on him because of the place that he had in their hearts, and in their front rooms, every Tuesday.

The way in which Bram became a Children's House broadcaster has been chronicled many times, and I have been unable to find an answer to the central mystery of the story. I did not really expect to find it but felt that I had to try. Eunice never knew who the "mystery man" was either. I will retell the story as it has been told to me: one afternoon Bram was walking down Market Street in Manchester when he was stopped by a man who had apparently recognised him from one of his talks. This man said that he was just what the B.B.C. was looking for to broadcast on the Children's Hour, and had he done any broadcasting ? Bram said that although he was used to addressing large groups of people he had never done any actual broadcasting. The man seemed surprised and said that he would give Bram's name and address to Olive Schill who was the Children's Hour organiser of the Northern B.B.C. Bram thought nothing of this and went on his way. It is incredible that this was the start of 'Romany of the B.B.C.'. Within only a few weeks there arrived at the house in Halifax a letter from the B.B.C. inviting him to attend an audition in Manchester, bringing with him some nature anecdotes he felt might be suitable. The audition went well and he was invited to take part in a live Children's Hour broadcast. The only problem was that the B.B.C. intended calling him "Uncle Bramwell". This he found rather severe and instead asked that he be known as "The Romany". This seems to have been a spur of the moment choice.

It proved to be inspired. The mystery of that name and the slightly exotic nature of the popular image of Romanies at the time gave the programme its essentially real and yet unreal flavour. On his first programme he was joined by Muriel Levy, Doris Gambell, Eric Fogg and Harry Hopewell. In this first programme he gave two five minute talks within the framework of the larger programme. These stories were about Phan the Otter and Brune the Mallard. The very first Northern B.B.C. airing of a Romany programme came on the 7th October 1932. The Radio Times said "We meet the Romany, and learn about the gipsy trail". The "Romany" was alternated with other Northern B.B.C. regulars such as Kookaburra and the Rosemary stories. It took only a few months for the Romany stories to become so popular that they grew into half hour programmes in their own right.

Adam the gamekeeper, played by Frank Nichols, had become an established figure before Romany began broadcasting, but he was soon edged out of the programme and the format of Romany chatting with Muriel and Doris with the occasional participation of Tim, Sally and many other characters from his own experiences became the norm. His talks became more "real" as sound effects were more widely used and his natural exuberance made him turn away from the microphone as he spoke, thus giving an "outside" feel. To enhance this effect the engineers faded the programme in and out at the beginning and end of each broadcast. This was so successful that when it was revealed in the Radio Times in 1943 that the 'walks' were actually taking place in a studio in Manchester, there was a storm of protest and many letters written accusing the B.B.C. of 'cheating'.

It was sad that this came only two months before Bram's death, but I do not think that it really had a detrimental effect. The talks became established favourites in the north and were always at the top of the list in request week. The only question that has been asked of me by so many people during the researching of this book is: "Why was the programme only heard nationally from 1938?". The answer to this has been a little difficult to find, although it seems to have come down to a personal clash of interests.

Derek McCulloch had become Head of Children's Broadcasting in November 1933, just a year after Romany had begun his broadcasts. He was known countrywide as 'Uncle Mac', and had begun his career as a children's broadcaster in 1929. He joined the London Children's Hour team on 1st January 1930 and very soon rose through Lord Reith's B.B.C. to become the guiding hand on Children's Hour right through to his retirement in the 1950's. He was told as early as 1935 of the huge popularity of the "Romany" broadcasts in the North. Why did he not allow the programme to be heard nation-wide until 1938? I believe the answer is that the technology did not exist to broadcast nation-wide from Manchester and so Bram would have had to move to studios in London's Broadcasting House in order to reach the entire country. McCulloch was also hosting a "nature" programme himself in "Nature Parliament". It has been suggested, most notably in Ian Hartley's "Goodnight Children Everywhere" that McCulloch was a little put out at the prospect of someone "stealing his thunder"; especially as his programme featured such notable figures as Sir Peter Scott and L. Hugh Newman. He may have felt that an "amateur" was not the person to be allowed a national forum for a programme of this type. However, in 1938 the popularity of Romany in the North and his championing by Nan McDonald proved too strong for McCulloch and at last children nation-wide were able to go "Out with Romany". It was not long before he was topping the requests on a national scale. It was not only he who was propelled to "stardom" but also Muriel and Doris and Raq the dog. Few people that I spoke to realised that the two "little girls" were also Aunty Doris and Aunty Muriel of the mainstream Children's Hour broadcasts. Raq was, in fact, only occasionally in the studio during the broadcasts and was imitated for the microphone by a very dedicated special effects staff that included Terry Cox and Jack Hollinshead.

As there were few recordings of the birds and animals encountered on the walks, these two had to make the noises themselves. It is not clear if Percy Edwards himself ever appeared on "Out with Romany" but the impressions that they made, usually taught to them by Romany himself immediately before the broadcast, were worthy of the great man himself. Changes were manifold when he began to broadcast nation-wide. The most dramatic was that his day was changed. Listeners in the North had become used to hearing Romany talk to them on a Friday, but the scheduling of the Children's Hour on a national basis meant that he had to move to a Tuesday evening. This was a wrench after six years at the original time and day and had no little effect upon the decision by the family to move closer to Manchester and to give up the church as a regular source of income. The largest factor in the decision to leave the regular ministry and move from Halifax was because of recurring ill health. Bram had been taken very seriously ill during a stay at the vardo on the North Yorkshire Moors and had spent a month in the Whitby Cottage Hospital. The problem , as always, was his duodenum. Bram always worked himself incredibly hard. During the ten years he spent in Halifax he still wrote regular nature features and articles for the Methodist Recorder and The Huddersfield Examiner who had continued his "Lure of the Open Air" column, still under the name of "The Tramp".

In October of 1937 he was reported to have been recuperating at Sandsend, and that his church work had been taken over by the Reverend Bramwell Howard. Whilst in hospital the Halifax church superintendent convinced him to return for his tenth year and to put off retiring.

This proved later to be a costly decision.

Having decided to return to Halifax, Bram initially seemed his old self, but soon the inevitable relapse occurred. This time the condition became so severe that it was decided that he should have an operation. Typically Bram was concerned about the arrangements for Raq whilst he was away in Manchester. Sadly this issue was taken out of his hands, as Raq died in his sleep a few days before Bram was due to go into hospital. The operation was successful, but pleurisy set in and he was very ill for the first few weeks. Once this condition cleared up, however, the change in his health and demeanour was wonderful. For the first time in years he was not on a strict diet and so was free to eat virtually as he pleased. The last year and a half in Halifax was a time that saw Bram in the very best of health. One of his first actions was to visit a kennel near the town and to return with a cocker spaniel that was the image of the last Raq. Very soon the pair had become inseparable and order was restored to his life once again. His article writing now included The Yorkshire Post and his popularity on the radio was huge. The Halifax Infirmary named their children's ward "The Romany" ward. It was with general sorrow that the community around King Cross and that of Halifax in general bade him farewell in 1939. Eunice dwells upon this point in her book and explains that he would from then on be an itinerant preacher, and thus there would no longer be the friendship and bustle of parish life for her. She says that she sensed the end of 28 years of closeness. Any time that she may have had for brooding on these thoughts was soon taken up with planning their move to a brand new house in Wilmslow. They had first seen the house in 1938 and had decided that its wooded surrounds and yet closeness to the B.B.C. in Manchester would provide the ideal home.

It is rather ironic that yet again the Evens family were setting out on a new and uncertain chapter in their lives just at a time when the world was tumbling into a global conflict; just as had been the case on their move to Carlisle. The new house was the source of great excitement for both of them. For Bram it meant that he at last had some land to call his own, and especially some trees that he could tend and observe every day throughout the seasons. For Eunice it represented the hither to unique opportunity to decorate their home entirely to her own taste, without having to apply to a church superintendent for permission or funds. The settling in period was not to be a long one, however, even before they had finished the unpacking they found that they were expected to look after two evacuees. After this the town was chosen as the site for an R.A.F. expansion airfield and vast numbers of the trees that had attracted them to the area in the first place were felled. Bram felt determined to "do his bit", and joined the A.R.P. Eunice was obliged to carry out his duties on the many occasions that he was away at broadcasts or lecturing. It is quite strange that Bram felt that he needed to do more for the war effort than he already was. The "Out with Romany" broadcasts continued during the blitz in London and the family received countless letters from people who said that the programme and his lectures and books helped to calm them during the darkest times. In addition to the work he had there the Wilmslow house became a sort of rallying point for all of the members of the forces who had grown up with his books and radio programmes and now found themselves billeted in the Manchester area. I think that the war meant that there was no real period of rest and retirement for Bram. Romany was as much in demand as ever and so his supposed rest time was filled by an ever expanding commitment to other people, outside the church, and outside of Wilmslow.

This is probably the time to examine how people reacted to Romany when they heard his broadcasts. It has been said by everyone I talked to that Romany did not so much talk at you, the way the other Uncles and Aunties were prone to do, but you felt that he was talking personally, just to you. When Romany said "Stop. Look at that" the listeners craned their heads towards the radio set to try to see what it was that Romany was describing. The style that Romany introduced is now familiar to all of us. He was followed by "Nomad" on the Children's Hour and then George Cansdale who survived up to the time of Blue Peter on television. Gerald Durrell, David Bellamy and David Attenborough all owe much to him. I think that Bramwell Evens was the first of this century's "great communicators". He was a first class orator, and his Evangelistic skills would surely have ranked him with his Uncle Rodney, the famous Gipsy Smith. Some people who were fortunate enough to have heard him preach in the Huddersfield and Halifax areas think that he was better at moving an assembly and taking them with him than Billy Graham.

I think the only question that every single person has asked me is: Where can I buy a recording of a Romany broadcast? The sad truth is that you can't. There is only, officially, one recording of an "Out with Romany" in existence today. I have heard the programme and was touched by it. I have also found 'snippets' of another programme contained in a documentary made about Romany by B.B.C. Radio Cumbria in the early 1970's, so there was at that time at least part of another one around. I have not found the B.B.C. of very much help during the preparation of this book. There were only able to tell me of the date of Bram's death and then refer me to The Authors and Writer's "Who's Who". One would have thought that after twelve years of broadcasting there may have been more help there, sadly not, however. The recording that does exist is not one of the best programmes according to Romany Watt, as it is one of the very last broadcasts that he made, from October/November 1943. It does show how well he worked with Muriel and Doris and does indeed sound as if it could be an outside broadcast. I was taken in and could imagine the hedgehog he refers to and all of the sights and sounds. Inevitably the physical artefacts of Romany are confined, in general, to his books, although I have heard of people with one of his thumb prints and a hair from one of the Raqs. This is, I feel, a little beyond the pale. In my own personal collection I have some books with his signature and a page from an autograph book labelled "Romany of Children's Hour. Golcar C. of E. School. Jan 21st 1939". This was sent to me after the Huddersfield Examiner featured my research. The most important and precious things in my collection, and the things that really determined me to write this memoir, are the countless letters that I have received from all sorts of people who had remembered him so vividly. These letters range from the simple "I remember hearing him on the Children's Hour and your cutting in the paper brought back some happy memories. Thank you". To people who actually knew the Evens family and had personal anecdotes and wrote of the fun they had with him. It may be human nature just to remember the good things, but not one single letter had anything but love and praise for him.

Here is an example of what I mean. This letter came to me in 1991 from a lady in Huddersfield who is well into her seventies:-

"Rev. George Bramwell Evens came to Buxton Road Methodist Church when I was twelve years old. Mother, Father and seven children, of which I was the next to youngest, were all members and we children attended the Sunday School. Mother was a member of the Women's Meeting and Father of the Young Men's Class. I remember Mr. Evens for his sermons and lectures and lovely sense of humour. The Chapel was always crowded and everyone enjoyed the Services.

I and five other friends spent a holiday at Robin Hoods Bay and had the pleasure of visiting Mr. and Mrs. Evens in their caravan at Sleights and having tea with them.

Just after he came to our chapel I was standing outside, one Sunday morning after the service, when he came up to me and asked if my mother had been to seen Mrs. Harrison who was ill - and did I know what was wrong? I replied "Yes, she has a Strangled Inertia". Which should have been "Hernia". He roared with laughter and proceeded to pass on this joke. At first I was covered with confusion, but he soon put me at my ease.

He used to visit us and other members of the congregation, and if it was baking day he always took fresh baked bread home with him.

I don't know if this is of any help to you - but I wanted to express my appreciation of his ministry. God Bless You."

It is interesting to note that this lady makes no connection between her minister and the man who was later to become so famous on the wireless, or who wrote nature columns for the local press. This surprised me: to the people of his parish Mr. Evens was just their minister, they all knew that he was a broadcaster and that, even when he was known across the country, he would remain special to them. This was a very strong part of his appeal and uniqueness. I doubt whether there is a personality today like that. This letter owes all to his ability as a preacher and a communicator. There is little doubt that much of his skill as an orator came from his mother and Uncle Rodney.

His congregation were not only aware of him as their minister but there was clearly a greater feeling that they had been fortunate enough to have been blessed with a man of extraordinary compassion for his fellow man and all of nature around him.

Another tale that was told to me was of a man who remembers being chastised in the gentlest way by Bram during a service at Buxton Road. He remembers that he had a cold and had been sniffing and trying to clear his nose throughout the sermon. Suddenly Bram stopped preaching and said: "If you will stop blowing your trumpet perhaps we can get on with the service!"

Bram died on the twentieth of November 1943. He was out in his garden all morning and came in complaining of pains in his chest. He had had similar pains before , and they did not seem too severe and so he went upstairs to lie down on his bed. Eunice stayed with him until he seemed more at ease, she then went downstairs to do some house-hold chores. Half an hour later she went back to see how he was and he had passed away. It seems strange to think that Romany died in bed rather than out in the vardo in the middle of the countryside. I don't think that Romany did die then, however. The Reverend George Bramwell Evens, Wesleyan Minister, wife of Eunice and father of Glyn Kinnaird and Romany June certainly did pass over on the 20th November in Wilmslow, but Romany has never died. I have proved that there are hundred of thousands of people in this country who still keep Romany alive in their hearts. When his death was announced on the six o'clock news millions of tears were shed all over Britain. The following weeks Tuesday Children's Hour was introduced thus:

"This is the B.B.C. Home Service. Hello, children. Today's Children's Hour comes from the North where we have all been deeply shocked to hear of the sudden death of Romany. Long before listeners in London, Wales or Scotland knew of him, he was a firm favourite with children in the North of England, and 'Out with Romany' always came top of the list for request week programmes.

During the last few years, however, and especially since the beginning of the War, Romany has made friends in all parts of the country, and scores of letters are coming in from listeners both young and old, telling us how deeply he was loved and how much he will be missed. I'd like to thank all those who have written, both on behalf of the B.B.C. and of Muriel and Doris to whom many of your letters are addressed. We will do our best to answer them all, though I am afraid it may take us some time to do so. Meanwhile, listeners who live in and around Manchester may like to know that a special Memorial Service is being held tomorrow, Wednesday, at 12.15 in the Albert Hall, Peter Street. It's almost opposite the old Free Trade Hall.

Our programme today is a Children's concert given by the B.B.C. Northern Orchestra with Dale Smith and a Choir of Manchester Schoolchildren. Ronald Biggs is conducting and will tell you about the music. But instead of beginning the programme as we originally intended, we are going to play a special piece as a tribute to Romany. We haven't chosen anything sad or funereal, we didn't think that Romany would like that, but the music we have chosen is full of the freshness of the countryside. It was written by Delius, a Yorkshire composer - Romany was a Yorkshire man, you know and like Romany, Delius loved the English countryside, the woods and hills and rivers, and captured in his music the same sort of atmosphere as Romany created in his broadcasts. He too thrilled as he listened to the song of a bird, and so we have chosen his Rhapsody on Hearing the First Cuckoo in Spring. Perhaps you would like to imagine you are Out with Romany once again as you listen to it."

I do not think that any listeners to Children's Hour could have failed to have been moved. The memorial service was packed, with people standing in the streets outside. The newspapers that carried the story were swamped with offers of a new home for Raq. In Bram's wallet after he died was found scribbled a short note:

"Nobody ever grows old merely by living a number of years. Years wrinkle the skin, but to give up one's enthusiasm wrinkles the soul."

After his cremation service in Manchester his ashes were taken to Glassonby near Penrith and scattered to the wind. It had been one of his last wishes that his ashes be allowed to spread over the Cumberland Fells that he loved so much.

The impact of his death was huge. Many schools, in the North of England, closed for the day. It is quite strange that he had already told his wife that he would be writing no more Romany books, and had finished the last only a few days before his death. When he finished the final chapter he went to the cinema with Eunice and a friend. This was out of character, but he enjoyed the outing. If he had listened to the repeated advice of doctors over the years then he might have lived longer, but it was surely mot in his nature to sit idle when he could be in the open air doing something. For him to have been working on his beloved garden, rearranging the rockery right up to a few moments before his death seems appropriate.

Bram left ten books, many articles and countless enraptured audiences, both of "Out with Romany" on the radio and from his lectures and preaching. He also left a loving wife and two children. Most important of all he left a love of nature and a warming kindness that has abided over fifty years, and will continue as long as there is anyone with a mind that is clear and eyes and ears that are open to the beauty of nature and the wonder of all God's creatures.

The Rev. George Bramwell and Mrs. Eunice Evens upon Bram's appointment to Carlisle in 1914.

The Methodist Central Hall, Fisher Street Carlisle.

The Memorial Tablet in The Central Hall

Gala at Buxton Road Chapel, Huddersfield, 1926.

Eunice Evens in Halifax 1937. The backbone of the
Romany books and broadcasts, and orchestrator of
parish life.

1st August 1911. The wedding of Rev. G.B.Evens and Eunice Thomas, Dalston Congregational Church, London.

THE BELLS OF SPRING

GETTING up early has quite a number of advantages. To begin with, it gives the early riser such a virtuous glow. This lasts well on towards late afternoon. Those who arrive downstairs later do so with a half apologetic kind of look as they meet the breezy individual who knows that he saw the sun rise. ' It is the early bird which catches the worm,' we say. Until I knew that worms were nocturnal in their habits I always thought it was particularly hard on the worm to be caught first thing in the morning. Now I know that it is the belated worm returning home that is caught. Not the early riser, but rather one which has developed night-club habits.So perhaps he deserves to be penalised,

How I came to be up so early in the morning need not be told. Suffice to say that Raq and I were by the side of the wood when all things were grey, when the wood itself was nothing but a cold dark shadow, and when the hush which precedes the dawn was not broken even by a sigh.

But the beasties of the night know by the universal grey dawn that their reign is over. The fox makes for his lair and the otter returns to his holt. Claw and tooth, often red with their adventures, steal into their retreats, where shadow takes the place of night.

Quite suddenly, the greyness takes on a warmer, pearlier tone, for across the eastern sky there streams a streak of daffodil light. Like a long trumpet it stretches across the heavens, its mouthpiece in the lips of some unseen herald proclaiming that, though sorrow may endure for a night, yet joy cometh with the morning.

Up from the wet meadows the lark begins to soar, and his silvery cascade of song breaks the spell of quietness. Now a blackbird gurgles out from a high elm, a thrush flings out his morning challenge, and then the whole orchestra of the hedges and fields is let loose. A mighty infection runs through every dingle and copse. Warblers, robins, hedge-sparrows, rooks, magpies, finches, all join in the merry roundelay of morn, until the ever-rising sun calls them to the more prosaic work of home-making or of family ties.

Out in the field, and some distance from the wood, I noticed Raq pointing with his nose at something on the ground, as his pendulum was working at a furious rate, I interpreted it that he had found something of interest.

When I arrived on the spot I could see nothing, and I fancied that he must have found the place where a few odd partridges had been lying during the night. However, as he persisted in his excitement and kept cocking up his eye at me, I looked closer, and then saw that the earth had been disturbed.

Going down on my hands and knees, I soon found a camouflaged hole, and the dog, seeing that I was investigating, immediately began to dig with his front paws, kicking out the loosened soil with the vigorous strokes of his hind legs. Not wishing to scatter the earth too much, I pulled the dog away, and soon found a burrow running underground. Here at the end was a warm nest of down, and in it I felt a number of young rabbits.

I brought a handful to light. Naked, blind little roly-polys they appeared to me, as unlike the pretty youngsters which gambol at the top of the big burrows as it is possible to imagine. But for them, the doe robs her own breast of her soft fur, and no doubt she thinks they are the handsomest children ever brought into the world.

As I looked at them I remembered the fable of the snipe, who, meeting a sportsman with his gun, implored him not to shoot any of her brood. On his asking how he should know them, she said that he could not make a mistake, for they were the handsomest birds he would meet. An ugly bird got up on the wing, the sportsman's shot rang out-and it was a snipe he shot. For a sportsman's idea of beauty is one thing, and a mother-snipe's is another.

Even so must the rabbit view her youngsters with very partisan eyes. Probably whilst I was delving into her temporary home she was watching me from some thicket. For the doe feeds her young at dawn, and then, covering up and smoothing the entrance of the hole, leaves them till nightfall. On her return they will poke about her with tiny pink noses, and, though they cannot see, yet Nature has endowed them with a keen sense of smell, and it is more than probable that they locate the source from which they receive their milk supplies by the aid of those absurd little noses.

Raq sat by me watching them squirming. His grave eyes had a look in them, however, which told me that I had but to say the word, and those hapless, helpless youngsters would have been trans-ferred into a corridor from which there would have been no return. So I carefully replaced them in their downy retreat, and did my utmost to cover up the tracks and traces of my soil dislodgement.

If, however, the nose of some prowling badger should come that way in a night's meanderings, I would not give much for the safety of those helpless rabbits. Neither would he take the trouble to dig out the front door. His sensitive nose would locate from the surface just where the young were lying. A few quick strokes of his powerful spades, and all would be over. 'Brocky' would be ambling away with a smile on his face very similar to the one worn by a very oft- quoted tiger.

Later in the day we came across Ned, the postman, and, as usual, received a hearty invitation to accompany him on his rounds. He had a wholesome respect for letters, but a hearty contempt for postcards. He was always annoyed when he had to trail to some distant farm and hand in a printed card.

On the other hand, he would often hold a letter in his hand and say to me:

' If I didn't deliver that 'un, the whole course o' history might be changed.'

Then he would tell me something of the two lives that he was linking together, and what might happen if he failed in his trust.

'I'm a livin' shuttle,' he would say, 'and I'm weavin' these two threads together, and, when the " piece," is finished, old Ned will have had an 'and in bringin' out the pattern.'

Sometimes I found it rather enjoyable when, amongst a particular heavy bag of correspondence, he could not at once find the post-card which he was about to deliver. As he was searching in its depths he would say to the farmer's wife who stood waiting :

' Ah, well ; it's just to tell you that Mary and the babby are aw reet, and that she's comin' ower at Whitsun to stay wi' yer. She says as 'ow she's got all her clearin' done, and as 'ow- But here it is, at the bottom as usual. But you'll find out the rest fer yersel' mebbe.'

As a matter of fact, had Ned lost the whole batch of his post- cards, he could have delivered their messages by heart to their varied owners. But never by any chance did he reveal the contents to any but the destined recipient.

'What a month this is,' said Ned to me, as we walked by a certain spinney. ' You told me just now as 'ow you saw the first stream o' sunlight shaped like a trumpet. Look at these first spring flowers- ever notice how many of 'em are bell shaped ? '

Even as he spoke there came over the still air, faintly but sweetly, the sound of a far-off peal.

'A weddin' mebbe,' said Ned, stopping to listen.

'How the sound swirls and sways,' I murmured.

' Look around ye,' he cried. ' In nearly every hedge ye'll find a nestin' bird. The robin's in the hole in the bank, the wild duck is sitting ovver there on fourteen pale-green eggs, the swallers and the martins are hastin' on their way with the thought of family joys speedin' 'em on.'

He paused a moment as though he were weighing up whether he should divulge his inmost romantic ideas. Then he continued :

' Well, it seems as though Natur' fits in with these bridal doings. Look at these early flowers which appear, So many of 'em are droopin' bells, as though Natur' were ringin' 'em on their way. When the west wind blows, I watch the snowdrops, the little woodsorrell of the pine-woods, the tall daffodils, and bluebells, all of 'em ringin' a car- car-' I expected the old man would fumble about for this word, so I was ready for him.

' Carillon,' I said quietly, so as not to interrupt him. But I spoke so softly that he did not quite catch the word, and thought I said, ' Carry on.'

' Carry on ? 'he said scornfully, and almost glaring at me for spoiling the poetry of his ideas with such a prosaic phrase.

'Carillon,' I repeated in a louder voice.

' Aye, that's better,' said he, mollified, and smacking his lips over the word for which he sought.

' All of 'em ringing their carillon-bells for the birdies' weddin's, swingin', swayin', pealin' ; and the great big marsh marigolds and the flaniin' buttercups standin' up straight out o'the green grass and holdin' their cups-' ' Chalices,' I suggested quietly.

' Holdin' their chalices aloft and cryin', "Good 'ealth to bride and bridegroom." '

The old postman finished with almost a sigh, gave a shrug of his shoulders, as though ashamed at having let himself go, and we walked on in silence. But the old man had set a peal ringing in my heart, the music of which will vibrate for ever.

As I walked home through the village I happened to pass a well- kept garden, the owner of which I knew slightly. Being full of the ideas which Ned had given me, I stayed for a moment to chat with him as he moved amongst his varied and well-trimmed beds.

I must say I never felt very drawn to the man. Once he had bundled Raq out of his grounds in a rather too forcible manner for my liking. But, with the music of Ned's bells still ringing in my ears, I felt I wanted to pass on some of the melody to someone else. Thus was I ensnared into telling him of the quaint conceits of the old postman.

'Ah, yes,' he said in his superior way; 'very pretty, no doubt. But we botanists like to stick to facts.'

' Facts are not so beautiful as truth, sometimes,' I ventured to interpolate.

' Those of us who have a scientific bent explain things differently,' he said, with a superior air. 'You see,' he added, ' those tubular flowers of yours live under cold atmospheric conditions. By closing the petals much of the warmth which would be lost by radiation is preserved. The surface presented to the Arctic winds and dews being that of the involucral leaves, or bracts, of the calyx, which-'

Just at this point I saw, to my relief, that Raq had forced his way into the garden, and the scientific mind at once descended to the practical plan of evicting the dog.

Along by the roadside I sat down for a moment, and Raq came and put his velvet muzzle into my hand.

' Raq, old man,' I said, 'you saved me just now from perpetrating justifiable homicide.'

The old fellow knew not what I said, but the affectionate tone caused him to snuggle nearer to me, so that he touched me with every part of his shaggy body.

' Mark the contrast,' I continued. ' Wedding bells, carillons, golden chalices ; and involucral leaves, bracts, calyx-ugh ! '

Later, when I reviewed the day and its events with my wife, she finished by saying with a sigh and a shudder:

'That man would typewrite a love-letter.'

I felt somehow that it was a most apt description.

CARAVANNING

WHENEVER I mention to any one the fact that I spend my holidays in a caravan and tents, ninety-nine per cent. of my hearers answer in the same way: 'Ah,' they say rather wistfully, ' that is what I have always longed for.'

I have no doubt that at the back of their minds there is a certain idyllic picture of such a life. They see the August sun streaming down in splendour on grassy knolls and making deep shadows under the trees. They think of meals eaten in the open air, where the breezes waft about those spices which are usually sung about at foreign missionary anniversaries. Very few ever think that for such a holiday to be a success a certain temperament is demanded, and one or two of the party must have certain qualities. To begin with, unless you wish to 'pig it,' there must be one member of the camp with a naturally tidy mind.

The caravan is twelve feet by six. It is divided into kitchen and dining-room. It has a stove, drying-cupboard, wardrobe, store- cupboard, shelves, sink, and a hundred other things that are usually

found in a house with many rooms. It is, in fact, a tabloid home. Therefore, to ensure comfort there must be a place for everything, and then everything must go back at once into that place. A very similar state of affairs exists in the tents where we sleep and the tiny ' bathroom ' that is shaded by a miniature tent.

Of course, when I am off alone with Raq, with a small tent packed on my back, with the moors stretching out before me and no human dwelling for miles - then things are different. Economy in weight and comfort is demanded, and how I live then only the dog knows, and he never tells. But in a holiday camp things have to be managed differently.

In our family my wife is the tidy person. She has an orderly mind. 'Can you tell me where my collar stud is?' I ask.

For a second she turns the eyes of her mind on her inner card- index, and answers: ' You will find it in the chest of drawers in the caravan on the left-hand side in the smaller leather case.' Then she may add something which was not entered on the card index : ' You left it in the empty butter-dish on the dresser you know, dear.'

From which you will gather that my quality of tidiness is not of the same high level as hers. Also you can infer from such an incident how useful it is to have a dog who can tell no tales.

Of course, for a home to have two with such a disposition for orderliness might not be for the best. Were I similarly gifted with such a mania for tidying up I should, were I to pass through the kitchen and find one or two cooking utensils lying on the table, immediately put them back on to their lowly shelves. This might be trying for the cook.

Then I could foresee both of us secreting a duster in some pocket in order to flick off the slightest speck of dust which we met with as we moved about the house. Also we should get to the stage where, before entering, we should both of us change our boots or shoes and creep in on slippers. The time might come when, in order to keep everything spotless, we might sleep out at a hotel to save soiling the sheets. From which you will gather that I look upon myself as a corrective to over-scrupulousness.

Looked at in another way, I am a contributor to her happiness, for if there were nothing to tidy up, her light would be hid under a bushel. How comforting !

When day has swooned into the arms of still night, then the tent awaits us. We light the storm lamp, and, as we walk towards its open flap, the beautiful silken creatures of the night air flit around its brightness.

Within two minutes I am in bed, revelling in the shadows which the lamp casts upon the sides of the tent. As a foil against this flickering warmth is the vision that can be seen through the open flap. The light catches the leaves of a neighbouring tree, and they twinkle like small mirrors. Behind them stretch out dark branches, swarthy arms of some giant octopus always reaching out, reaching out, ever grasping, but never holding.

Behind them lies indigo night, and on her dark bosom heaves the filmy necklet of the Milky Way, a coronet of blazing stars, far away, lest their brightness blind the eyes of mortal men.

But if there is poetry and romance there are other things too. My wife takes longer than I do to snuggle between the blankets. There are tiny black specks on the sides of the tents, some of them just over her bed. These must be examined. They might be beetles.

'Now see you put them away tidily,' I say, ducking my head under the clothes, Pick them up and put them on the grass outside. A place for everything and everything in its place.'

' What's that ? 'she asks, pointing to some moving object on the wooden floor.

' That,' I answer, 'is a ferocious beast more terrible than the tiger, more to be feared than the panther or the shark-it is an earwig.'

She shudders and hops into bed with alacrity.

' Did you look in your bed ? ' I ask, just as I turn out the light, and seeing she has settled down quietly. ' What for ? ' she asks sharply.

' Oh, nothing,' I answer casually. 'Only I noticed-'

'Noticed what ?

' That you hadn't examined it, that's all. Good night, dear, and don't forget that weasels and stoats, foxes and rats, and all the little creatures of the night are more frightened of you than you are of them.'

For a few moments longer we lie quietly listening to the noises of the night. Meanwhile I take up the role of interpreter: 'Kevit,kevit.' The sound comes from the adjoining field, not raucous, but mellowed by distance.

'Owl,' I murmur,' probably the short-eared one, flitting like a ghost over the field, and every mouse and vole shivering with fear as the big-eyed one floats past,'

'That's the fern-owl or goatsucker,'

I say, as a low, churring note intrudes itself. 'He's after the moths. Opens his mouth wide like a great net, and seeks rest by lying flat upon some bare branch.'

Away in the distance a shot rings out. Its echoes roll down the glen.

'Poacher ? ' asks my wife.

'It may be,' I Say, ' but more probably some keeper is keeping watch over his young pheasants. Most of them are not yet roosting in the trees where they are out of harm's way. He is there to ward off prowling vermin.'

'It's not the known it's the unknown that is rather uncanny,' she says, as she finally turns over and settles down to peaceful sleep.

For a few moments longer I listen to the voices of the night. Down through the velvet dusk there falls the double pipe of a passing bird. A moment later an answering call comes, a plaintive single note.

'Curlews' I mutter to myself, ' making for the coast where the tide will leave long reaches of wet sand.'

In my mind's eye I can see the birds with their long, curved bills reaching out towards their feeding grounds, the leader every now and then giving the note that tells the rest 'All is well'. Perchance the answering call is to assure the company that in spite of the darkness and the speed there are no stragglers.

After the curlews come the oyster-catchers or sea-pies. In the darkness they are but dark blurs which for a moment blot out a star and are gone. But in the daylight they are in startling black and ivory uniform, whilst an orange bill splashes them with continual sunlight.

My mind dwells on the sea-pies. I remembered how disappointing my experience with them had been. I had found a nest with four speckled eggs lying amongst the sandhills. It had been difficult to distinguish which were eggs and which was gravel. But I had erected the hiding tent hoping for the best, only to find that the birds were too shy, and to save desertion I had moved on.

With the next nest I had similar ill-luck. Finally, however, I found a nest belonging to a pair of bold birds. Very soon they accustomed themselves to the curious growth which had sprang up in a night and kept moving nearer to their treasures.

Then, on the morning when, after carrying all my heavy impedimenta, I had reached the tent, hope singing in my heart, I had glanced at the nest, my expectations had all been dashed to the ground-the eggs were broken. A sheep had walked right on them. Only a pair of disconsolate sea-pies hovered on the sandhills, emitting at times a note which had in it all the elements of reproach.

With such reminiscences in my mind, I went to sleep, only to dream of unbreakable eggs, oyster-catchers which met you on the sandhills and conducted you to their invisible nests, and scorning such a necessity as a hiding-tent, posed for the camera in as many interesting positions as they could think of. Alas ! It was but a dream !

In the morning over breakfast the family chat cheerily over the prospects of the day. At least they do this after they have exhausted the tale of their night's adventures. It usually consists of how they evicted daddy-longlegs, heard various wild beasts seeking to find admittance to forbidden territory, of various moths and midges which tried to snuggle down on their faces.

Then the question arises of how the day shall be spent. Secretly I hate this part of the proceedings, for I do not like to know how I shall spend the day. To have it scheduled out and the hours allotted for various enjoyments is misery to me. I prefer to set out like Abraham, not knowing whither he went, and yet finally coming precious near to the Promised Land.

Finally, all vote to go to the seaside. Of course, I am outvoted and submit, though I gaze anxiously at the hills to see if I can find a cloud, even though it be no larger than a man's hand. But the horizon holds no promise of rain and I am forced to predict a day of sunshine.

For the next three-quarters of an hour the camp buzzes with relentless activity, Certain necessities must be taken. Every one, too, drawing on past experience, remembers something else which woul make for comfort on the beach. It goes down on the list, and usually finds its way into father's pack.

Inside, the van is like a caterer's kitchen. The kettle is steaming ;thermos flasks loom in the offing; piles of sandwiches await their wrappers.

Then comes the offensive for the bathing requirements. Each child, having contracted the habit of sitting down in the sea just when its rubber protection has been taken off, must have two changes of raiment-towels, buckets, spades, ' woollies ' for warmth, paddling shoes, bathing costumes, rubber caps, rugs, books for reading.

Finally, everything is ready, and under a relentless sun the caravanserai sets off looking like a brood of ducklings, father bringing up the rear in order to pick up stragglers and stray packages. I look back at the camp. How peaceful it all seems. Beyond is the brook where the dipper will be curtsying on its stone near the waterfall. Over the hill a kestrel is quartering the dry ground and swooping with unerring flight at its vanishing quarry. I can see the tops of the pines gently swaying in the morning breeze, and know the quiet of its glades, broken only by the small chatter of the tits and the drone of a million small wings.

But the beach lies ahead, where the promenade is littered with people who spend their time in moving from one seat to another, where all the excitements of city life are exaggerated, where cinemas and pierrots, dances, and theatres, tennis and golf, make the sea with its glory just an after-thought, an accessory to pretty frocks, an excuse for herding together round its golden strand.

As for me, I usually deposit my family near the tide and forget the conventional mob round about me. We sport in the sea, and then I find some quiet nook where I can watch the terns dive after the white bait, and the herring-gulls float without effort on the tides of the air.

Sometimes I hear the cry of the kittiwake. Then for a time I am far away from the surging crowd. I am on the cliffs of Ailsa Craig and hear again the chant of the gannets and the nursery cries of the nesting kittiwakes. The children play about me, the bathers may scream and laugh to their hearts' content. But my inner self is wandering amidst the places where the foot of man seldom treads.

THE BALANCE OF NATURE

I OUGHT to say at once that I am a 'tramp' by choice and not of necessity. Lingering in the city either to gaze at shop-windows, or to be regularly amused by some 'show,' is not my highest form of bliss.

I prefer to loiter in green meadows, to explore the fringes of quiet pools and the margins of laughing streams, to muse under shadowed hedges-in a word, to potter about where the wild birds sing or where the trout rises to the fly.

As a companion, I have my dog Raq. I take him, firstly, because a spaniel is the most loveable and sensible thing on four legs, and, secondly, because the alliance between my sight and his nose is a very strong one. What I miss in the bushes he points out. He stands like a statue before any discovery, his eyes questioning mine, and, according to the interest of his find, even so works his stubby tail. Should it be a hare lying snug in its' form,' then his tail works fast and furious; if it be a mouse, then a few mild jerks is quite sufficient for the occasion.

It was with him that I found myself one morning walking along a path which leads through a wood. Like a well-trained dog, he trotted contentedly at my heels.

On all sides the quietness of those shadowed aisles was broken by the protests of those who resented our intrusion. A pair of jays were not only resentful, but positively abusive, and hurled at us every epithet in their bird vocabulary. I saw the flash of their saxe-blue markings as they dodged behind the hazel-bushes.

Farther on, the wood-pigeons, sometimes called 'cushats' or ' queece,' launched themselves from the pines, and, in order to give warning of our approach, clapped their raised wings with resounding smacks.

Even the wren was annoyed by our progress, and creaked out her petulance as we penetrated deeper into her sanctuary.

Finally we reached our objective-a small hut in a clearing, and here we waited.

The dog lay down at my feet. How differently each of us got into touch with the world around us ! I was limited to what I could see and touch. Even my hearing could not be compared with his.

I watched his moist muzzle. Now it twitched to the right, and he knew that a pheasant was moving in the distant undergrowth. Now it veered to the left, and told him of a rabbit that lay crouching in its ' seat ' under the blackberry-bush.

Then he raised his head, and his tail, working slowly at first, nearly wagged itself off as there came to my ears the steps of him whom I sought as he made his way to the hut.

I would like you to meet John Fell; that is, if you are on legitimate business, for he is the gamekeeper of the estate.

There are gamekeepers and gamekeepers. Some there are who only know their own particular line of business. They know how to rear a few pheasants, they can level a gun at what they call 'vermin' and perchance can train a dog. But John knew the call of every bird, could interpret every track left in sand or mud, and was a sure hand at branding everything with feather or fur on it, as friend or foe. He had only two hobbies-his work and his Church.

' Anything fresh ? ' was his greeting to me.

This did not mean that he wished to hear an epitome of the morning's paper,

' Well,' said I, ' there's a heifer calf arrived this morning at Whiterigg; during the night a fox has killed two ducks and seven pullets of Jim Doyle's ; and I saw them up at the Blue Farm starting to thatch.'

He nodded appreciatively.

' Ye've an eye and an ear for the country,' he said ; and, seeing that he was in a good humour, I offered him my pouch. (This was good strategy on my part to get him to sit down and have a crack.) But he shook his head, and said, with a smile :

' I like a smoke,' and forthwith he proceeded to cut, from a fearsome-looking slab, slices of black tobacco.

Whilst he was filling his pipe I was gazing at the side of the hut, against which were suspended a few carrion crows, magpies, sparrow-hawks, and an odd stoat or two.

' How is it,' I asked, pointing to the ramshackle carcasses, 'that you shoot so few of what keepers call ,vermin"? I have seen scores of stoats, weasels, kestrels, owls, and sparrow-hawks outside other keepers' huts ; you have the poorest show of any I know.'

' Well,' said John, taking a deep pull at his pipe, 'I believe in the balance o' Nature'.'

I sat silent, as I knew he loved to open out a phrase, and I also knew that if he were not in a talking mood nothing would induce him to open out.

'The balance o' Natur',' he continued, 'is a pecoolier thing. Some as don't believe in it. I do.'

He picked up a straight twig, laying it at right angles across his first finger, as though to illustrate his words.

'Ye see that bit o' wood ? 'he asked, looking at me from underneath shaggy brows. ' It's lyin' straight now, 'cos both sides are equal. I shove this side a bit, ye see, and toother 'un cocks up. I've made a mess O' the balance.'

I nodded, knowing that he hated to have his moods fractured.

' So it is with Natur',' he said. ' Everything alive, if we but knew it, balances one another. Rats'll eat partridges, and partridge chicks, But the weasels and stoats come along and kill the rats. Mice come along and do a deal o' damage to cornstacks, but the owls come out at the rising of the moon and pick up thousands of mice. The sparrerhawk snatches the small birds from the hedges, but we should be owerrun with 'em if they didn't. Shoot all the swallers to-morrer, and what'll ye do with the insects swarm next season ? I'm speakin', o' course, in a general way.'

For answer I took up a straight twig, and, as it lay on my finger, cocked up one side more than the other.

He smiled and added, 'That's what 'ud happen on this estate if I shot every weasel or stoat that popped up in front of my gun. No doubt they take a few eggs, and perhaps a few chicks, but, if ye haven't too many about the place, they pay for their keep. Destroy the nateral enemies of the rats and mice if yer like-but ye have to pay the price o' their increase.'

After I was sure that he had finished, I said 'That reminds me of something you may have heard of. A few years ago the farmers in Scotland were alarmed at the appearance of a plague of voles. There were hundreds of thousands of them. All their crops suffered, and it seemed as though they would all be ruined,

' So threatening was the menace that the Government was appealed to, and they tried to discover some means of coping with the plague. But, before they were ready, Nature found her own remedy.

' Into the devastated districts there came swarms of the fiercest enemies of the voles. The owls came in their hundreds. The little red hunters, the weasels, ran amuck amongst them; kestrels poised in mid-air, made their relentless swoops. What the Government could not do, talon and beak, tooth and claw, did. And the result ? '

Here I simply pressed down the cocked-up end of the twig and restored it to the level on my finger.

John smiled delightedly at the story and its confirmation of his own ideas.

' Ye talk about yer wireless,' he said. ' How did those owls and hawks know that there was abundance o' food for 'em in Scotland ? Who sent the S.O.S. to the weasels and the stoats ? ' He paused for a moment. ' There's a text fer ye-" Withersoever the body is, thither will the eagles be gathered together." '

The keeper's pipe was out and his chat ended.

' So long,' he said, and, with firmly planted strides, went off to his duties.

'Cheerio,' I replied. ' See you again soon.'

When I was alone I turned to the dog, and as I began to speak he sat up and looked at me with soulful eyes, whilst his noble head, with its long ears, reminded me of the pictures of Egyptian Rameses,

' Raq, my lad,' said I, ' you have just listened to a phrase which contains a good deal of wisdom, and I hope you took it all in.'

The dog's tail began to wag furiously. He might not be able to understand what I was saying, but he liked its bantering, caressing tone.

'The Balance of Nature-that's the theme. It hints that the universe is run on a compensating system. If anything lacks something, then some other thing is added to keep the twig level. " What you lose on the swings you make up on the roundabouts," as Aristotle or Harry Lauder said.

If you have a wet summer you may still get good root crops, turnips and mangels ; if dry, then a decent harvest of hay and corn.'

As I walked on I kept that phrase before me. A thrush poured out its heart from an elm, and a kingfisher flashed, like an emerald, up stream. The former is not much to look at, but what a voice ! The latter has no voice, only a grating ' Zit, zit,' but what robes ! I applied the gamekeeper's idea, and found it illuminating.

A little later we sat down together to enjoy our lunch-it was Monday's fare-a few sandwiches made of cold meat. At home we should have turned up our noses at it or had a poor appetite.

But how different is its flavour when you eat it sprayed with the lark's music, seasoned with the curlew's plaintive pipe, and scented with the wild thyme which blows from the fells.

Then my eyes fell on a paragraph in the paper which had been a wrapper for my lunch. It stated that a big prize was being offered to any gardener who could produce a rose that was not only stately in poise, fine in texture, and royal in bloom, but possessed a fragrance. Evidently it was difficult to coax Nature to endow one rose with all the qualities of colour and scent. If it had magnificent petals, then it lacked the languid odour that the ragged white roses possess which grow in profusion over cottage doors. Here evidently the gamekeeper's idea was again being verified.

'Aye, Raq, my boy,' said I, turning to my faithful companion, ' that's a grand phrase-the Balance of

31

Nature. It speaks to me of the stars in their courses,
    of wind and tide, of summer and winter, of garlands and wreaths, of the sorrow that comes at night and of the joy which breaks with the dawn, of life and death.'
    I paused for a moment, and then quoted quietly to myself, ' For God hath set the one over against the other.'
    Just so ; the Balance of Nature is but another name for the equipoise of God.

A YULETIDE DECORATION

IT was a beautiful morning, and Nature had decided to give the world a real Christmas covering. Snow had fallen during the night, and when the fields lie under their white counterpane, then is the time to learn what the wild folk have been doing. For a few hours a newspaper of their secluded lives is spread for all to read, for wherever they have moved, they have left behind them a record of their wanderings.

Here is a rabbit warren, and around it is a bewildering network of footprints. The tracks clearly point to the fact that these little creatures have been perplexed at finding all their feeding-places hidden by the snow. Some of the knowing ones have scratched until they found a little verdure. Most of them, however, went back to their dark corridors as empty as when they left them. They had never seen snow before.

By the wood are the broad three-toed marks of the lordly cock- pheasant, and where his tail trailed on the ground has been faithfully registered by the glistening whiteness.

In the centre of the stubble-field is a dark, circular patch. On examination it proves to be a circle where the snow has been thawed. Here, a covey of partridges has spent the night, tail to tail, heads turned outwards and forming the circumference of the pack. What disturbed them, and why they fled with a great whirring of wings, may be seen by the far hedge. There lie footprints, compact as a cat's, and giving the impression that they had been made by a one-legged creature. They are the tracks of a fox who had looked greedily at the birds, which he had scented a score of yards away. Happily for them, their sentinel had not slept, otherwise there might have been a few chestnut feathers blowing over the field, and perchance a few red drops staining the virgin whiteness that covered all things.

Nearly all living things are at a loss what to do when snow falls. Even Raq, as he trotted along, showed unusual listlessness. There was no scent left behind of any living thing, and a spaniel without a scent is as useless as a hawk without eyes. He brightened up, however, as the village came into view. Here he knew that he would come into his own again, even though we only explored the byres and barns.

And so we walked down the quaint village street, and, as we journeyed on, faces appeared at windows and doors, and voices flung me a nosegay of the season's compliments.

'Come in ; have a bite o' summat' said one of the many hospitable souls, and, knowing that sooner or later I should have to capitulate to their importunities , I entered the cottage of Sally Stordy.

' Fancy bein' out in sic' weather,' said my hostess, and when I told her how I enjoyed it she added, 'Well, every man to his taste.'

Soon I was seated before a table on which lay a couple of smoking rashers. Raq was contenting himself with a bone.

'You remember Sarah Ann ? ' asked my benefactress.

'When did she die? ' I asked guardedly, not being able to recall the owner of the name, and judging by the tone of the questioner that something tragic had occurred.

' We killed her-that's 'er ye're eatin',' said my friend, taking off her apron.

For a moment I had an inward sinking sensation. Then, with infinite relief, it dawned on me that Sarah Ann was the name of their sow, and one which I had often admired.

' She were a right good 'un, she were,' said she, with a sigh.

' She is,' said I, interring pieces of Sarah with relish.

'We shall never see 'er likes agen,' the good soul said regretfully.

'Never again,' I murmured, as I finished my repast, and, in spite of its flavour, feeling that somehow or other I had been present at a memorial service.

' Here's a slice or two for your missus,' she said, handing me a good-sized parcel, ' and here is a bottle of " cleat " wine. Made it myself. No need to be afeard on it. It's teetotal.'

And so, fortified within and without, we went out into the snowy roads. What splendid, unspoilt souls these country folk are ! Silver and gold have they none, but such as they have, give they unto you.

We called at the home of Ned, the postman, and, finding that he was going to a neighbouring village, we set off with him. When we were leaving the last of the houses behind us, I turned to him with my stock question 'And what have you been thinking out lately ? 'He was about to answer when a troop of boys and girls came round the bend of the road, two of the boys bearing big armfuls of holly.

'And what have ye been up to now, you young rascals ? ' asked Ned of the uproarious group.

' Getting 'olly for the school-to 'ang it up,' said one of the boys.

'Aye,' said the old man, ' I see you have.' Then he paused a moment and continued: 'And you got that bunch, Dick Thompson, from pretty near the ground; and yours, Jimmy Dale, had to be climbed for.'

' Yer right, Ned,' said the boy Dick, with a tone of admiration in his voice. ' Jimmy had to get up a rowan-tree to reach the lump he has. Tell us, how did you know, that ? '

The old postman smiled and shook his head. 'Not now ; haven't time to stop and talk to ye.

Ask me another time and I'll tell ye.'

And so we passed on, and I knew that within the next few days Ned would be seated on a favourite stone with his back to a barn, and round him would be grouped a bunch of inquiring and interested youngsters.

I determined to press the question which Dickie Thompson had asked,

' But how did you know from what parts of the tree the holly had come ? It looked pretty much all the same to me.'

For a moment or two Nod made no reply. Then he turned towards me and said :

'You believe in disarmament and the League o' Nations, don't ye?'

I do,' I answered heartily.

'Well, the holly-tree, if you study it at all, will give you a few points which you can think about. Have you ever thought that this world '-here he raised his arm and swept fields, dales, rivers, hedges, woods into his embracing thought-, have you ever thought that all of it lives, so to speak, on a war footin' ? '

' Well,' I said, ' I have in my own mind divided all animals into the hunters and the hunted.'

'Aye,'said he, 'that's allright. But even the plants , shrubs , and trees must be included. Ye must not only think of the stoat after the rabbit, and the kestrel after the mouse, but you must think of the cattle as bein' the enemies of everything that grows. Do you think the hedges want to be eaten ? '

' I hadn't thought of it in that light,' I answered.

'Ah,' said the postman, with a chuckle,' but many of the trees 'as, and they've met the danger with foresight and cunning. Well, now, take the holly as a sample. Here is a tree which knows that when writer comes round it'll be one of the only green things left standing in the fields. Around it'll be nothin'

34

but stripped hedges and tasteless, sodden grass. It knows, too, that every cow or horse that's longing fer a taste of some green thing will single it out fer special attention. So its chances of escape are precious few.'

He looked at me to see whether I was following his statements.

' I follow you, Ned,' I said, and I added, ' Of course, the real trouble of the tree is that it cannot take refuge in flight. It is tethered to one place.'

' That's it, exactly,' said my companion. ' Well, then,' he went on, ' just as the nettle has its stinging needles, so the holly- tree has turned itself into a kind of green hedgehog, and nothing with a tender, sensitive nose ever thinks it worth while to tackle it.' We trudged on in silence for a few, minutes, and, thinking that the old man had finished, I said :

' But that doesn't explain how you knew from what part of the tree the youngsters had cut their bunches.'

' I'm coming to that, ' he said abruptly, so abruptly that I felt for a moment that I myself was attempting to browse on a holly- bush. I had forgotten that he did not like to be interrupted save when he invited it.

'Now, every bush knows that it can't do two things successfully. If it grows prickles--defences--it can't put all its strength into its leaves or fruit. If ye 'ave yer armaments, something must suffer. If ye spend five million pounds on a battleship, ye can't have it fer eddication.'

He paused, and I saw by his look that at that moment I was expected to say something.

'I've been reading quite lately that cattle experts say that experiments go to prove that hornless cattle make more beef and better quality than horned ones. They say that the growing of horns is an appreciable drain on the beast's strength. No horns means better and more meat.'

' Mebbe that is so,' said Ned, ' though I'm not fond of "cush" cows myself. Howsomever, the holly- tree acts as though it knew this ; and now comes the answer to them boys and girls. The leaves of the tree which are nearest to the ground and just where their danger of bein' eaten is the greatest, have the most prickles on. But, when you look at the branches above seven or eight feet high, you find that the defensive points are not so numerous--in fact, in some holly- bushes they aren't to be found at all. So you can see how easy it was fer me to tell them childer where their bunches grew. Dickie Thompson's lot was nearly as prickly as a gorse-bush so he had to do no climbing to get it. Jimmy Dale's had more berries on and less spines so he had harder work to get his'n.'

We left Ned to do his business in the village, and Raq and I branched off into open country.

Ned's explanations about the holly had certainly been intriguing. I could not help wondering whether the bush had developed spines in order to defend itself from its enemies, or whether, somehow or other, those prickles had come into existence in the ordinary course of development. Then the natural result would be for all 'browsers' to avoid it. Could the plant think out a plan of campaign such as Ned had hinted at ?

And yet Sir Jagadis Chandra Bose, the Indian botanist, who has specialised on plant life, tells some uncanny facts concerning the mind of the plant. He has registered its heart-beats, stayed its death by poisoning, and has witnessed its response to stimulants. I thought of the pine-tree and its exuding resin the latter takes the place of our bandages for a wound. When the tree is cut , the gum covers the gash and wards off damaging bacteria. Chance ?

I mentally inhaled the scent of varied plants due to the manufacture of various volatile oils. They attract the insects that are necessary to fertilisation yet are fatal to bacteria- fascinator and sanitizer in one. Chance ? The rhododendron is green during the winter, but plates itself with silica, so that anything that swallows it suffers from internal pains and avoids it ever afterwards. Are all such wonders due to something more or less fortuitous, or is there a glimmer of intelligence behind it ?

Be that as it may, life for them is a struggle, and out of the struggle issues vitality, inventiveness, patience, persistence.

THE LURE OF THE OPEN AIR

AUGUST

I Do not remember a time when the countryside had no fascination for me. Give me a lane and a hedge, and heaven lies in exploring its shadows and becoming intimate with its shy inhabitants. Probably this is due to the fact that I spring from pure gipsy stock. In my veins runs the blood of nomads who have sought the solitudes for hundreds of centuries. It is this ancestry which has made me ,a roamer, and like a bird hearing its migratory call, so the fields and the woods lure me from city life.

I know what it is to climb the stiff cliffs of lonely Ailsa Craig, to listen to the chant of the gannets as I photographed them on the narrow ledges which overlooked the sea four hundred feet below. I can hear again the cry of the kittiwakes and oyster catchers as I neared their nests on other lonely islands of the Scottish coasts. Yet of all the places I have visited, there is none which yields me so much content as rambling round the countryside.

Could you take a peep at my caravan, where it now rests, you would see it shadowed by boughs on which the apples lie thickly and heavily. By the side of it runs a hedge where the bees lumber cumbrously on to the bramble blossom, and where the ' lintie ' sings a plaintive litany as she sways on some slender bough. Just behind the tents runs the stream. I can hear its tiny tinkle even as I write. A very subdued yet high melody it is singing-the melody of a thin string, of shallow waters, of attenuated channels. All its dryads and nymphs are for the moment tremulous sopranos.

But the hoped-for rain will come ere long and the tone will change. The ringing of its bells will give place to a roar and hiss of triumph. Then from their lairs will issue forth the big trout. Up from the neighbouring river the sea-trout will sock its yellow waters, thirsting for the flavour of the beck which perchance first gave them birth.

My caravan has a history. It has rumbled along the roads and lanes and heard the chatter of the Romanies as the light of the camp- fire lit up their swarthy faces. I am reminded of them by the big box attached to the rear. This big receptacle was most useful when passing turnip or potato fields-not to put many in at once, that was not necessary, for there were plenty of other fields to be passed, and the box would still be there !

That hook on the axle is where Boz, the lurcher, was tethered, and under which, when any strangers were about, he used to lie as meek as a lamb. In their presence, he cultivated a slight limp and had the knack of looking prematurely old. But as soon as their backs were turned, a rejuvenated Phoenix
would have looked antiquated beside him, especially as he ' sleuthed ' it up the hedge side.

The hook is still behind the van, but the lurcher that never barked, and never knew when he was beaten, is now in other happy hunting grounds , R.I.P.

As I lounge by the caravan steps a flash of green and scarlet streaks through the trees, dodging the trunks with marvellous precision. Then from the end of the orchard there comes a joyous ' yaffle.' It holds in its tone satisfaction and derision. I listen for a moment and then hear a definite strong tapping of the wood. It is the green wood-pecker, at work. He owns the orchard too. When, in the thousands of years that have rolled by, his ancestors determined to seek their living on the barks of trees, with occasional relapses in the direction of ant-hills and marshy ground, Nature fashioned their bodies to suit their habits.

The All-Mother has been very generous to him and his kind. She has made him a specialist in the art of probing. His bill is a strong drill. From where I sit I can see him driving at the tree-trunk. I cannot see the individual drives, so fast does he withdraw and strike, withdraw and strike. All I can see is a blur of green and cardinal. Then I can hear the reverberating thuds.

Could I crawl nearer I should see that his tail is very different from that of the sparrow chirping from the caravan roof. Indeed he uses it almost as a stool, and, pressing it firmly against the bark, sits on it. With his two feet such an arrangement makes an excellent tripod stand. Steadied thus he searches with his long telescopic tongue for the hiders in the bark.

I would like you to see that tongue, for on the end of it is a barb such as you find on an angler's hook. Feel it, and you will notice that Nature has dipped it in seccotine. It is a harpoon for the struggling larvae and the stickiness picks up the smallest of fry.

Look ! He is-but the bird has caught my slightest movement, and with a derisive chuckle is lost in the neighbouring trees. When night draws down her curtain on the orchard in which the caravan rests, then the fire is lit. With Raq my constant companion, a spaniel with an animal's sensitiveness and a human being's understanding, I sit and watch the pine logs flicker. The incense rises, and as the smoke curls upwards into indigo night, I see the faces of those who love the countryside as I do and interpret its phases to me.

Away up in the fields I hear the call of the ewes to their lambs and my mind flies at once to the farm where Alan and Joe live. What hospitality Joe's wife and the sisters offer to me ! How great is their never varying welcome.

Then the silence is broken by the bark of a fox, and in spirit I am with John Fell, the gamekeeper. That bark, I know, will make him uneasy about the safety of his young pheasants, and I can see him walking round his sanctuary in the hope of heading off the sleuth of the woods. Soon, from the stream behind me, I hear the plunge of a sea-trout, and I wonder whether my friend John Rubb, is bringing any to their doom by his skilful casting of the ' fly.'

I think also of Jerry, the poacher, but not a 'ne'er do well.' I marvel at the queer nature of the man which endears him to all who know him even the keeper is one of his friends. As I think of him I envy, too, the rich store of knowledge which he has of every bird and beast. I envy him, too, his lovely thatched cottage which nestles on the fringe of a wood. Musing thus, I feel how blessed I am in my friends. Who would not delight to go with Ned, the village postman, as he delivers his letters to distant farms, and to listen to him as he unfolds the marvels of insect, flower or pond life ? Then there is Sally Stordy whose cottage is a refuge and a rest, and whose quaint outlook on life and her sound common sense is a joy to listen to.

I love the smithy, too. To begin with, it has a smell all its own. The byre has its own fragrance ; so has the barn. No one can mistake the floury dry mustiness of the granary. But the smithy is a mixture of burning horn and scorching leather.

Of course, the blacksmith has his work to do, and does it well. But what the shop and post-office are to the women of the village, the smithy is to the men-folk. It is the unofficial B.B.C. of the district.

There is, too, an air of timelessness about its smoke-grimed walls, and here and there are unconventional seats worn smooth and bright by the corduroys of its habitués. Talk flares up at intervals, even as the bellows call on the slumbering fire to wake up and glow red, and the smith, even though he be beating out a merry tattoo on the anvil, still manages to catch the spicy tit-bits of gossip as newcomers drop in and range themselves amongst the shadows.

At the village shop, smoke seen issuing from an unused chimney is sufficient to keep the ball of gossip rolling for a whole morning. Who knows but what it may portend the arrival of a visitor, or perchance that fire burning through the night may mean that a new bairn has arrived. The absence of the usual smoke from Sally Stordy's washhouse will call forth a torrent of questions as to the reason for this departure from the usual.

But in the smithy runs the rumour of a new kind of threshing- machine which Dick Pennington is getting, or men speak in admiration of the price which Jim Sheppard received for his lambs.

As the darkness deepens in the orchard then the bat swings round and round in uneven undulating circles. Above the top of the grass the white moths are doing the ghost dance. The owl leaves the warm barn, and after sitting motionless on some bare branch sweeps down with deadly precision towards the darkening grass.

The stars are out and the last pale shimmer of light shows from the top of the hills. I go towards the tent and throw myself on the bed. I can see the Pole Star and Great Bear blinking at me through the open flap. The hayrick sends to me its final benediction. The world is drowsy, only a young cockerel mistakes the hour and begins to crow prematurely.

Now, too, the brook is singing its sweetest lullaby. A distant train I can hear rushing to some town where poor folks are sleeping in stuffy rooms whilst I am bathed in the wonders of a velvet world. Ah, well ! I must turn in.

THE REVELATIONS OF RAQ

I Am a Spaniel , and I would rather be that kind of a dog than any other in the world. I once overheard my master say, " There is no more intelligent or loveable beast than a Spaniel." That is why I am so content.

Many people say that animals cannot think or reason. That is why I am putting down a few of my thoughts on paper. To begin with, I was born in a big box, and though I do not remember a great deal about it, yet some things do come back to me. I was brought into the world blind, but I could wriggle about from the first minute. Perhaps that is why I was born with my eyes shut-so that I shouldn't wander very far from the warm nest. I knew that I was not the only one, for I could hear other little squeaks and feel other wrigglers roll on to me. The only things that I was really conscious of were : firstly, a big warmth that it was jolly to be beside, secondly, a big hole in my inside which this 'big warmth' had the means of filling. The ' big warmth,' of course, was my mother, and I cannot describe how beautiful was the milk she gave to us. Though I could not see, yet I could smell, and that is how I used to nose my way to the source of supply. I always fought for the same place at meal-times. The best place was nearest to our mother's head, and the weakest of my brothers and sisters always got pushed lower down to the other end. I believe those ill-behaved creatures which 'humans' call pigs refer to the weakest as the ' runt ' or the ' wreklin '-at least I have heard farmers refer to them as such.

It was a great day for me when my eyes were opened. I believe I was nine days old at the time. I remember it because somebody came and picked me up, and I felt the first touch of fingers and the cold chill of the outside air.

But as soon as I was back again in the box my mother licked me all over. This was not because I was dirty, but because she said that it was dog's custom never to let any human scent remain on young dogs. She told us that puppies themselves had a scent, but that if they lay still it grew very faint, and so any passing enemy went by without doing any harm.

When we asked her why we had a scent at all, she told us that we should learn the reason fully when we were older. Of course I now know that it is one of the ways whereby dogs recognise one another. With a good breeze blowing I can smell one of my own friends quite a field away.

As we grew older, so we were able to move our legs about and see better. At first we could only distinguish light from shade. Then we could see things that moved. Finally we were able to distinguish everything that was near at hand.

When this time arrived, then our mother used to encourage us to play and tumble about together. She brought to us a piece of rag and we used to play tug-of-war. Then we had mimic battles amongst ourselves, and sometimes the play would get rather rough. Then sometimes our mother would growl out her displeasure, and I have seen her nip one of my brothers with her teeth.

' You'll need all your strength in the big outside world,' she used to say. ' So play on. You will find out what you can and what you can't do. As it is all in fun and nothing depends on it, failures don't matter. But in the big world outside, failure oftentimes means suffering and death.' So we used to struggle and play for hours on end, and I could feel my soft flesh turning into muscle and my limbs getting bigger and more firmly set.

Now that I am older, I can see the value of these play-hours. I did not know what I was doing at the time, but now I am grown up I do in the emergency what I have learnt in fun-and do it with confidence.

Just take, for instance, that greyhound who lives down the road. When he was a puppy I have seen him chasing his brothers and sisters in circles. That is how he learnt to swerve and turn quickly, and now when he hunts the quick-footed hare, he knows not only how to turn, but what speed in turning is safe.

Of course, we were taught other things. When we went for a walk with our mother, she used to put her nose deep down into things which were harmless, and we used to smell it after her, and store up the smell in our brains. Humans store up all kinds of things in their minds. They know their houses by their numbers or names. We know them by their smells.

But if a thing were harmful, our mother would put her nose down to it, then she would lift her head and walk away. Sometimes her tail would stop wagging, and then we knew that what she had found was very injurious. Human beings are eye-minded and ear-minded, but we dogs are nose-minded. We live in a world chiefly of scents and smells. When we meet one another we do not say, as my master does, ' How do you do ? ' or talk about the weather. We ask, ' Good scenting ? ' ; and if the scent is in the air, we raise our noses, if strong on the ground, we turn our muzzles downward.

As soon as ever we could trot about as puppies, our first instinct was to follow the big one that protected and fed us. That is why we like to attach ourselves to human beings. Perhaps there is a deeper reason too, for I remember my mother telling us that thousands of years ago all dogs lived like wolves in packs, and followed a trusted leader. I believe she said that at one time we were wolves, but had developed into something better-just as my master's ancestors were once monkeys, and now he is a man.

But the other reason why we love human beings is because we do not like being alone. We are not individualists, like cats who live for themselves and themselves alone-selfish spitfires, who love places rather than people, and who only live near to human beings because they find them their food easily. In those far-off days my mother told me that we all lived in packs, and so we have a sociable nature and can enter into family life. That is what makes us such good watch-dogs. We do not bark to keep people awake at nights, but because it is in our nature to warn the whole pack if we think that we scent danger. You have never heard a cat giving the alarm at night. Also, I think, that we are restless at nights because when we were in a wild state our great foe used to prowl about-I mean the leopard, who liked nothing better than a dog for his supper. I have often wondered whether our dislike and suspicion of a cat really grew out of our hatred of the leopard, for this animal is nothing more than a big cat, and belongs to the same family.

It was a great day for me when my master came and chose me for his very own. He looked at me and my brothers, and then, picking me up, said, ' That's the little beggar I want,' and I knew by the very feel of his fingers and the tone in his voice that he loved a dog.

That, by the way, is how we understand most of what humans say-by the tone ; not merely by the words. I like my mistress, but she always puzzles me because she issues her commands in different words. My master says 'Seek,' or 'Fetch my slippers,' and I know what he means every time. But my mistress says, ' Go into the kitchen and bring your master's slippers,' or ' Your master wants his slippers.' Fortunately the word ' slippers ' is an easy tone to remember, and gives me the clue.

4 1

But what a curious new world I had come to, and how quickly I was expected to learn a thousand different details. I might go down the steps which lead from the kitchen to the garden, but I was not allowed (at least when my master was out) to go upstairs in the house. He used to take me up into his study, and when my mistress was away from home I used to sleep in his bedroom at the foot of his bed. What interested me most was the way he used to take his outer skin off, so that I hardly recognised him except by his scent before he got into bed.

Then I was expected to know whom to bark at and whom to wag my tail at. My mistress scolded me one day for growling at a friend of hers, but I didn't like her at all, and I knew she didn't like dogs, although she tried to pat me.

Once when some visitors came to the front door, I growled at them, and was sent to the kitchen in disgrace. They had a good meal in the dining-room, too, and I heard them laughing and talking. But after they had gone I heard my mistress say, "Weren't they dreadful people ?" Now if she disliked them so much, why ever didn't she let me send them away from the door when they first came as I wanted to ? These are the sort of things that puzzle me.

If I meet a dog and we are not on good terms, I don't let him come near me. I just show my teeth and put up the fur round my neck. That is generally a good enough warning.

Again, all my food is put on the floor in a basin. But how can I be expected to know that it is the only dish I may touch. There is one wonderful small room, white and clean, with a lot of shelves in it. Oh! what appetising odours issue from under the doors-stews-gravies-joints. But if I find the door open and some pan or other on the floor, I'm not even allowed to skim the top of it with my tongue -and in dogdom, "Finding's keeping !" I love my master, but he has such curious ways. People say that animals are ' creatures of instinct and habit,' and do everything without reason. But just think what funny things he does. Sometimes when he comes to dinner I have heard him say,' Oh ! I'm not at all hungry.' But he eats his dinner all the same.

Now animals never do that. You never find them eating when they aren't hungry. Human beings eat just because it has become a habit with them. Then they wonder why they don't feel well.

Then as I sit in the dining-room I wonder at the different kinds of food that they mix up together. At first I thought that my master would choose one of the dishes and no more. If he were a dog he would have chosen the meat, and have eaten that and nothing else. But he mixes it with potatoes and sodden cabbage or turnips. Then, on top of -it all, he sends down custard and apple-pie, and sometimes he pours coffee on the whole lot. But animals never eat and drink at the same time.

If my master's boy or girl doesn't feel well, he gives them drugs and medicine. I've noticed that he always tries it on them or on my mistress first.

That is another thing which proves how unselfish he is. We animals, however, rely on a good starve when we are not well, and drink big draughts of cold water.

Another thing puzzles me. My master is very fond of washing himself. He even uses a flashing knife to one part of his face. But he never thinks of washing his inside as well as his outside. We dogs, however, think even more of that than we do of our skins, and so we drink as much water as we can hold, and whenever we can. I don't think I ever remember seeing my mistress drink any cold water. She always heats it up first, and colours it a dark brown.

Talking about being in the dining-room at mealtimes reminds me of another thing which took a lot of learning. Sometimes my master would give me a little piece of meat, and my mistress would say-' You know, dear, you should not feed that dog in here.'

I used to think that he looked a bit frightened when she spoke like that, but he soon recovered. I've been with him at all hours of the day and night, and I used to think that he was absolutely fearless. I've seen him playing football, and the way he knocked over big men proves that he has tremendous courage. But a little sentence like that seemed to bowl him over. If he had a tail, I'm sure he would have dropped it between his legs, just as I do when I feel nervous. Why he doesn't use his football strength at such times puzzles me.

Then I've heard my mistress say, ' That dog does bolt his food ravenously. I wonder why he eats so badly.'

She forgets that it is my nature to eat like that. A cat is a solitary creature and hunts alone. Consequently she can take her kill away to some quiet corner and eat it leisurely. There is no one to share it with her. But we dogs, being members of a pack, used to bring down the buck or the sheep, and immediately it belonged to us all. Those who could eat quickest got the most. Those who ate slowly, if there were any, went away hungry.

The best time of my life is when we go to live in tents. Sometimes my master packs up a small one, and then he and I go off together, eat together, sleep together.

Then it is that he even dresses differently. There is no stiff white collar round his neck. I can't understand why he has this on, for every dog hates a collar-it is the sign of servitude, and my master is no slave. I have even heard him call it a ' dog collar,' and I know by his tone that he hates it too. Once when it lay on the ground I saw some printing on the inside, so perhaps that is his name and address engraved on it, like some of our collars have. Perhaps, not being able to scent his way, as we can, he easily gets lost in the streets of a big town.

Then when we go off alone, he leaves his heavy boots in the tent, and for hours goes about unshod, even as I do. His hat, too, is put on one side, and he walks about a real man.

But as soon as we get back to town again, all the old things are back again in their places. It is a pity that he is such a creature of habit.

Then, too, I've noticed that my mistress has curious ways of dressing. She, too, wears an outer skin like my master, but she moults far oftener. When I compare her with the other women in the streets I notice that she is wearing similar colours and similar shapes. In fact, there is as much sameness in women's skins as in men's, only, as I say, they cast their skins oftener.

This is because they are like dogs, members of a pack, social animals.

You see, in our original state, all wild dogs were brown. Such a colour hid them from their foes. If a striped dog had appeared they would have chased him from the tribe. Why ? Because an odd-looking dog would have made the whole pack conspicuous a prowling leopard would have noticed the striped one, and so the pack would suffer. And so every dog has to be like his neighbour. If he isn't, he suffers.

I suppose that must be why my mistress, along with other members of the herd, all dress alike. The leaders of the pack must meet somewhere and decide what the colour and shape of the new skin is to be. Then the commands are issued. I have noticed that my mistress is continually receiving circulars with colours and patterns of what she calls frocks on them-so these must be the orders issued from headquarters. Very few indeed dare disobey these commands, for , if any of them dress differently they are like a striped dog in a pack,and get unwelcome attention. Humans call it' being out of fashion,' whatever that may mean.

I went to a show once, and, by the way, got a red ticket-First prize. But all the dogs were amused at the manner of judging. The shape of our heads, length of ears, straightness of legs, clean feet, the way we carried our ears and tail-all these were taken into consideration.

But the real test no one ever called for. The nose is the real test of a dog. We ought to have been made to retrieve something, to find our way back ten or twenty miles from home, to detect the criminal from the law-abiding citizen. Not features, but qualities and virtues, ought to fit us for a prize.

Then there were ' little microbes '-I call them :toy-dogs lying on cushions and having great bows of ribbon round their necks. What a disgrace to dogdom ! Their bleary, bulgy eyes and snorting snub noses made them good for nothing but a lady's lap-unhealthy little beasts. I dare not allow myself to write down what I think of them.

Only one more word will I write. I love being with my master at all times. I have heard him say many times, and I am very proud when he says it, ' The more I see of men, the better I love my dog.' Whether he takes me in the fields or in the town, it is all the same to me so long as I am with him.

But the best time is when he sits in his study quietly alone. Perhaps he is reading and having a smoke at the same time.

Then I like to draw up near to him and just touch him somewhere. It doesn't matter what part of him I touch, so long as we are in contact.

Then his thoughts run into me, and I think mine do into him. He says he owns me, and so he does. But I own him too.

EARLY LAMBS

THERE was still a good deal of snow lying about as I set out for the farm. It was hard walking, and I slipped more than once. Where the dog had walked I could see the deep marks of his claws, and admired Nature's resourcefulness, giving him such non-skid feet. On some roads the snow-plough had been at work, and I was thankful for the relief it gave in walking. I left the road at one point and cut up by the side of a hedge, but after extricating Raq from a snow-drift, I decided to keep to the well defined paths.

After passing a cottage by the roadside, a carrion crow flew up from the bottom of the hedge. He carried a white egg in his strong beak. He was so close to me that I could actually see how he carried it. It was not between the upper and lower bill, as I expected, but the cunning old rascal had thrust his lower bill through the egg-shell, and then closed the upper one on it.

I slipped through the gate, and searching in the bottom of the hedge found a hen's nest with seven eggs still left in it. So I walked back to the cottage to inform the owner.

' There's a " doup " just visited the nest up there, and carried away a hen's egg,' I said to the woman whom I knew by sight.

'Was it by yon gate? she asked.

'Yes, and those left will not be there long if you leave them.'

' It'll be yon Ancona that's bin layin' away. I've noticed 'er slinkin' off a time o' two. But she's that cunnin' I've not bin able to find'er nest. Thank ye fer tellin'me.'

' I shouldn't leave them very long,' I said, 'or he'll get the lot. You'll find which nest it is quite easily as I've trampled the snow down round it.' At last, tired with the heavy walk, I caught sight of the farm chimneys, with their blue smoke curling straight upwards.

In the fields the black Galloway cattle had trodden down the snow. A shed stood waiting to give them shelter, but it seemed as though they scorned such comforts and preferred to trust to their shaggy coats, rather than to the roofs of man's devising.

Joe was just entering the yard, and he gave a whoop of delight as he caught sight of me.

'Well, who'd have thowt of seein' you oot on sic a day,' he exclaimed.

' I thought you might all need digging out, so I came along to do my good deed,' I said laughingly.

'Come in and have a warm. Sally's got summat as'll set you goin' again.' And so round the table we sat enjoying the good things brought out of the larder.

' I suppose the lambing season has begun, hasn't it? ' I inquired anxiously.

'Aye, we're just nicely started. About a dozen have arrived,' said Joe.

'And how many have you-ewes, I mean?'

' Two hundred, so there'll be a bit o' work afore they've all settled doon with their fam-lies.'

' I was trying to tell a friend of mine what breeds of sheep you stock, but there seemed to be so many. I got as far as a Border Leicester Tup, but I couldn't for the life of me remember what breed the ewes were. I nearly said Shorthorns in despair.'

Joe laughed. ' Even yon couldn't cross an owd sheep wi'a milkin'   coo. What ye were trying to think on were mebbe Grey-faced Leicester Cross. We used to cross a Grey-faced Wensleydale wi'-

' Here, that's enough for the present, Joe.'

After a warm up, Joe and I went out to see the sheep, leaving Raq before the fire. Passing through the gate which leads from the farmyard, I recalled the view one gets in Summer. The land falls alway towards the river, not in sweeping flatness, but in rich heaving undulations, as though loth to lose its height. Almost every, summit is crowned with larch, pine, and elm. In the valley below, the river glides reflecting the moods of hills and fields. Then once again the land begins to rise, until at last the distant hills seem to hold up the very sky itself.

But no such view, spread out before Joe and me.

Only a white desert, relieved by trees, which stood out fantastically black and white.

'Do you bring in your ewes to some farm building when you are expecting the lambs to arrive?' Joe shook his head. ' We find they're better left to theirsel's. Some farmers with a small stock some-times bring 'em up to a Dutch barn, but we leave 'em oot.'

I watched two tiny straggly-limbed youngsters sheltering behind their mother.

'They look as though a puff of wind would blow them over.'

'Aye, ye'd think so to look at 'em. But as a matter of fact, once they get on their legs, and get a drop o' warm milk into 'em, it can rain, hail or snow, and they're all reet. If a new lamb's gettin' plenty o' milk, it can stand more cold than its mother can.'

Once again I stood and looked at them. Is there anything more appealing than to see those long tails waggling like catkins as the warm milk streams down their thirsty throats?

'The milk must be very rich to give them strength to resist the cold. Is it stronger than cow's milk, Joe?'

'I reckon it is, and if ye watch 'em ye'll find their motto is "Little and often." The lie o' this land is a help an' all. D'ye see how it rises and slopes? It means that whichever way t' wind blows, the ewes can get a sheltered spot. We allus cart the turnips to where it's warmest, fer sheep are silly things.'

'In what way do you mean, Joe?'

'They allus seem when left to theirsel's to get to the most exposed part o' t' field. I reckon it's because they never face a storm; they allus turns their tails to it, and so they get driven before it. So one of my jobs, every night, last thing, is to drive them to a warmer corner.'

The bleats of the lambs broke the silence, punctuated by the lower raucous bleating of the ewes.

'I should be tempted if I were a farmer to bring the sheep all up and put them under cover, especially if I had such good outbuildings as you have, Joe.'

Joe laughed.' There speaks the townsman, used to coddlin' hissel'.

'I don't mean you,' he added hastily, linking his arm in mine. ' But if I were to put a lot of ewes and their lambs together in a small space, we should soon be in bigger difficulties than facin' bad weather. Just picture what 'ud happen. Here's a - ewe with two lambs, and she's near one as hasn't any. What happens? The one as hasn't any pinches one o' 'ers. Then, mebbe, a few hours later her own couple arrives, an' she finds hersel' wi' three to look after.'

'Well, can't you give the pinched one back again to the rightful mother? ' 'Aye, it sounds easy enough, but the trouble is that the mother won't 'ave it back once it's bin separated from her for a few hours. So there ye are.'

We returned to the farm, to receive a great welcome from Raq. Then we went into the dining-room, where a huge log threw out its grateful warmth. Of course we had to eat again, and then have the usual ' crack,' but things did not seem quite complete somehow. Nothing was said. Then to our delight we heard Alan's footsteps and cheery voice in the kitchen, and the party round the fire was complete as of old.

Later we found ourselves listening to the wireless. When at home I listen to the weather report very casually, but how intently Alan and Joe listened ! When we heard the announcer foretell warmer conditions and more normal temperature, Alan said -' Hundreds o' farmers and shepherds 'll say "Thank God" when they hear that,' and I then realised for the first time what a boon such forecasts were in the country.

As I went up to bed I looked up at the distant fells. Had the shepherds before the big fall of snow received the warning of the wireless, and with their faithful dogs brought their flocks down to the lowlands in time?

' Star gazing? ' said Joe as he passed me on the landing. I told him my fears.

' I reckon there'll be a few sheep buried up there,' he said.

' That means a loss to the farmer,' I sympathised. 'Not always. So long as a thaw doesn't set in, sheep can live together under t'snow fer several days. Yesee, t'snow's light and doesn't shut oot the air, an' they come oot not much t'worse fer bein' under it, But thawing snow thickens an'smothers 'em.'

'But how can they find the sheep in such a wilderness ? '

' Ye fergit their dogs, brave lil' fellers. They'll scent 'em oot all right-an' then it's just diggin' work. O' course, there's allus other dangers when t' sheep is buried. Foxes are ravenous with hunger, and if they find them they soon get a meal, eatin' their legs first. Or if by any chance t' sheep begin strugglin' under t' snow, and then manage to poke their heads out-then mebbe there's a carrion crow waitin' to pick their eyes oot.'

The candle I had carried up with me warned me that it was time to say 'Good-night.' So I made my way to my room, where my feather-bed waited to envelop me. Candle light ! How beautiful it is. Electric light has its advantages, but it invites one to keep awake, whereas a candle is the essence of drowsiness. Electric light scorns shadows, and shadows speak of dreamland, mystery, and twilight, and are a rest to tired eyes.

Before getting into bed I looked through my window. There was a dark streak amidst the white of the snow, It was Daleraven Beck singing its song of eternal freedom.

HOTCHI THE HEDGEHOG

I ARRIVE AT THE FARM

MY caravan moved at a leisurely pace along the country lane. Raq, my cocker spaniel, sat with me on the driving-board, and I held the reins lightly, for Comma, my horse, needed little guidance, as she knew the way to Fletcher's farm, which lay farther down the road.

There are many ways of seeing the countryside. You can travel about in a car, you can pedal along on a bicycle, or you can use Shanks's pony. All of them have certain advantages, but if you have a caravan, you carry your home about with you, you can sleep where you like, stay as long as you like in some quiet lane or field, and then pack up and move elsewhere.

It was May, and the sun shone brightly on the fields.

"Come on, Comma, we shall soon be at journey's end ," I said. She quickened her step at hearing me speak to her. One ear she kept turned back in my direction, the other she pointed steadily forward.

"That is more than you can do, old man," I said to the dog. " You certainly have longer ears, so long that you could wipe your nose with them, but you can't move them independently, as Comma can." The dog knew by my tone that I was teasing him, and looked up at me as much as to say :

" True, Master, but you forget to mention the things which I can do, and Comma can't. Think how my nose points out to you the birds and animals which lie hidden in the hedges, and which you would not see if I did not rush them into the open." So I gave him a pat, and in a moment or two we drew up before the gate which led into the farmyard. I put the brake on the caravan, hitched up the reins, and, with Raq trotting at my heels, opened the gate. As I did so the old gander, who was sunning himself with the geese by the pond, instantly set up a warning note.

There is no better watchdog than this wise old bird, and neither dog nor stranger can approach where he is, without the whole neighbourhood being made aware of the fact. His strident tones made the farmer's wife, Mrs. Fletcher, come to the kitchen door to see what was the matter.

" Oh, it's you, Romany, is it ? I wondered why the old gander was making such a to-do. I am glad to see ye back again. Come in t' kitchen, and I'll mak' ye a bite o' summat." That was typical of Mrs. Fletcher.

Whenever she saw me, she always thought that I must be hungry, but I had a lot of things to do, so I said:

" Not this time, thank you. I want to unpack and pitch my tent."

"In the same place as last time " she asked.

"Yes, it's the best spot I know. I just called to let you know that I had arrived. Perhaps you will send Tim down in the morning with milk and butter and eggs, if you can spare them." Tim was Mrs. Fletcher's son, a boy of twelve.

"Aye, he'll be glad to come. He's been askin' for a long time when Romany was goin' to come back. He'll be runnin' down to ye as soon as I tells 'im I've seen ye. But send 'im home if ye don't want

48

, im. "

" Oh, let him come. He can help me put up the tent, you know. He is never in the way. I like boys."

So I woke up Comma again, and the caravan skirted a long wood, turned sharply to the right down an inviting lane, and came to rest where the pine woods halt at a stream. Raq knew every inch of the site, and I could see him sniffing at every bush in which on former occasions he had found a rabbit sitting.

After putting Comma in the shed-stable which stood in the neighbouring field, I started to un-pack. Out of my caravan I brought my tent and its pole, and straw for my mattress. The bed I have in the caravan I only use in the winter, when the tent outside would be an icehouse. Then I collected some large stones, and after forming them into a circle, I brought some dried leaves and wood and soon had a fire blazing merrily. Then I filled my kettle and hung it from the iron tripod over the fire.

Then up the path in the wood I heard the sound of running feet and Tim's voice.

" Hullo, Romany; I am glad you've come back again. Mother said you wanted me to help put up the tent." Raq growled for a moment at the boy, went up to him and smelt him, and then wagged his tail.

"He remembers you, Tim."

"But he growled at me, didn't he? " said he.

"Oh, that was before he recognised your scent. Dogs don't use their eyes as much as their noses, you know. We look at people and keep photographs of them in our mind, but a dog stores up scents and smells for future use."

"It's a queer way o' rememb'rin' people," was Tim's comment, as he patted the dog.

I pushed the tent-pole into the cap of the tent, and together we raised it.

" I see ye keep it clear o' the trees," Tim said, looking up at the pines.

" Yes, I don't like the tent to catch the drippings from the leaves after a shower; besides, mosqui-toes and flies find you out under trees. Now hold on tight to the pole while I drive in the pegs and fasten the guy ropes. Keep it straight up if you can."

In less than half an hour the tent was ready for my bed. Tim carried in some pine branches which I cut down. These made a springy foundation. Then we spread a rubber ground-sheet over them, and on top of this I put the straw, which, pushed into a bed-tick, made an excellent mattress.

" I could sleep there mysel', I reckon," was Tim's comment as I put my blankets on top.

The last thing I did was to throw a couple of sacks on the ground at the foot of the bed.

"That is for Raq, " I said; and now I'm ready for the night. Thank you for helping me, Tim; I don't know what I should have done without you."

"Is that all I can do, Romany? " he asked, just a trifle hesitatingly.

I think he was afraid that I should send him home.

" What about having a look at the stream and seeing what animals have been visiting it lately? " I suggested.

He brightened up considerably. " You mean to try and find their tracks left in the sand and mud? That would be fine! " So, with the dog trotting at our heels, we went down to the waterside.

" Oh, there's an interesting mark," I said, pointing to a small patch of clay on which was im-printed a curious looking paw-mark, all bones and joints.

Tim looked up at me enquiringly.

" That shows that a hedgehog has been out hunting after beetles. You can see where he has been nosing about under some of the stones."

" We kills all the hedgehogs we find on the farm," said Tim.

" What ever for?" I asked.

"Jim, the gamekeeper, says they does a lot of damage, and farmers say they sucks the milk from cows. So we kills 'em. Isn't it true, Romany? "

" The best way to answer that, Tim, is to see if we can find a hedgehog, and then watch it together."

"Do you think we can find one " the boy asked eagerly.

"I'll get Raq to work. I dare say his nose will be able to scent out one. Now I think it is time you were going home."

WE SEARCH FOR THE HEDGEHOG

THE next morning, just as I was finishing my breakfast, I heard the sound of running in the wood, and a moment later Tim appeared on the caravan steps. " I've got an hour afore goin' to school," he said with a grin. " Can I do owt to help? "

" You might help me to make my water-filter, Tim, if you like." So we went down to the stream, with Raq, as usual, following us.

" What's the spade for? " he asked.

For answer, I started to dig a hole about a half a yard from the water's edge.

" You see," I said, as I threw out the gravel , " the water from the stream is beginning to trickle through."

"It's a bit mucky though," was his comment.

"You wait a bit. Then you will see a clear pool. The water passing through the gravel acts like a sieve and strains out all the dirt. When the stream gets discoloured by rain, this little well will always be clear. Now, how much time have you before you go to school? "

" About half an hour, I reckon," Tim answered promptly.

"Then we'll see if we can find a hedgehog, shall we ?"

"That will be fine, Romany, 'Ave you an idea where it'll be? "

" Yes. You remember where we saw his tracks in the sand last night? We'll go down there. The hole in which he sleeps won't be very far away."

"But doesn't he go a long way from home to hunt for his supper? "

" No, not very far. He will prowl round a couple of fields or a short distance in the wood, and then when he's full up, he'll amble back again to his lodgings and go sound asleep. We'll go down to the field now."

Raq got very busy with his nose, but the scent was not too good, as a few hours had passed since the hedgehog had hunted there.

So we turned into a field which had a good hedge growing, and along the ditch bottom Raq hunted. Once a rabbit scuttled away out of a mass of roots, but fortunately Raq did not see him, or he would have wanted to chase him.

At last he put his nose down to a rabbit hole at the base of an old tree, between two thick roots. He sniffed and sniffed again, while his tail wagged furiously.

"There's summat inside," said Tim.

"I rather think it may be Hotchi."

"Hotchi ? " queried Tim.

"Oh, I often see this one about. She has lighter coloured quills than most of them."

"I thought it were a rabbit."

"Do you see this grass that leads down to the roots? Now, if you look carefully, you will see that there's been a kind of path made. Not a very clear one, but as though some clumsy animal had pushed its way through it. Can you see what I mean ? "

"Aye, I can."   "That is what a hedgehog usually does. He blunders on, and pushes down the grass with his spines. That is why I think Hotchi is sleeping in there. Now it's time you were off, Tim.

Come along this evening, and we'll come back here and keep a watch on the hole. That's the way to learn how animals live."

Tim appeared at my caravan long before the time that Hotchi was due to set out on her evening prowl, so I got him to help me gather a good stock of wood for my fires. Then, as the light began to fail, we set off for Hotchi's tree, locking Raq up first in the caravan.

It was a beautiful evening, with the moon already beginning to show above the hills. " It'll be a grand night fer seein' things," said Tim hopefully.

" And luckily for us the cows have cropped the grass fairly short, so we shall be able to see Hotchi when she comes out."

When we got about a dozen yards away from the tree, I threw a sack down on the grass for us to sit on. Away on our right the cows were lying, and now and then the evening breeze wafted their fragrant breath as they lay chewing their cud. Away in the wood we could hear the brown owl hooting, and in the low-lying meadows the peewits were crying to each other.

" Them birds never seems to sleep," said Tim. " I've heard 'em carryin' on when I've woke up in the middle of the night."

" I think they must sleep in snatches," I whispered, and Tim took the hint, and lowered his voice.

He was in the middle of telling me how many peewits' nests he had found in April, when, coming from the hedge, I heard a distinct snuffle, almost a grunt.

" Listen! " I whispered. " That sounds like Hotchi."

" Can you see anything? " asked Tim. " I can't. Oh, yes, I can. Something has just pushed the grass on top of the ditch-a moving black blob. " Coming nearer, the hedgehog grunted audibly.

" She's not afeared o' makin' a noise, is she, Romany ? Most animals, as they go about, are quiet, aren't they?" They are, " I replied. "You wouldn't catch a fox squealing out his plans. But of course the game birds have quick ears, and if he made a row they would be on the alert; but the hedgehog noses about for beetles, slugs, and any insects he may come across."

"My father says he eats eggs, and so does Jim. That's why they kills 'im, " whispered Tim.

" He does eat eggs, Tim, but I don't think he deliberately looks for them. If he comes across them as he is snuffling about , of course he'll gobble them up. Can you hear her now, poking her nose into every tuft of grass? Keep your eyes open. She's coming into the field."

"She'll see us."

"I don't think she will, if we keep as still as a stone. Hedgehogs haven't good eyesight. They use their noses mostly for scenting their food."

Tim chuckled quietly. "It's a good thing we left Raq in the caravan, or he'd have been after 'er afore this."

I nudged Tim, for the hedgehog was now within two or three yards of us. At first the wind was blowing our scent away from her; then a stray whiff must have reached her, for she paused for a moment with her nose feeling the air, then turned and scampered back towards the hedge.

"By gum, I never knew she could run like that ! I thought she were too fat to run."

" Most people think that, Tim. As a matter of fact, it would take you all your time to catch her.

Watch ! She has stopped over there by the ditch. Now she's moving on again. Let's track her." So we stalked the little hunter. Now and then we could hear her slicing a beetle which she had found, and giving a grunt of satisfaction.

A cow lying on the ground looked up in the semidarkness.

"Now we shall see whether a hedgehog sucks cows' milk," I whispered. Once or twice we saw her lift her nose into the air. Then the cow's scent must have come to her, for she left off searching in the grasses, and made a bee-line for where the cow was lying. When within a couple of yards, she paused, and began to search in the grass, moving in a circle around the cow, yet never venturing so near that her prickles came into contact with the cow's body. She kept her nose on the ground, and seemed to be having a good meal.

" What's she doin', Romany? " asked Tim.

" Getting her supper without much trouble; getting a free meal. You see, when the cow lies down, beetles, slugs, and other insects in the grass don't like being flattened out by her great weight move from under- neath her warm body   as quickly as possible. Hotchi knows this, just as starling knows that he will find ticks on a sheep's back. So she makes for the places where cattle are lying, to find insects."

Tim whistled quietly.

" I'll tell me father."

"You tell him this, too, Tim," I continued. "You know what a big mouth a calf has. Well, we'll have a look at a hedgehog's mouth some time, and you will see how small it is-too small to hold one of the cow's teats. Besides, a hedgehog has thirty-six sharp, pointed teeth! "

" I'll tell me father reet enough," was Tim's comment as we left Hotchi to carry on with her supper.

I saw Tim to the edge of the wood, where the path leads directly to the farm, and made my way back to the caravan.

HOTCHI CLIMBS THE WALL

I ONLY saw Tim for an hour or two in the days that followed, and during that time we never caught a glimpse of the hedgehog. On the Saturday morning, I called at the farm to get in my store of butter and eggs, but found that Tim had gone into the village to do some errands for his mother. So I left word that if he was free in the afternoon we might go out together, and see if we could find Hotchi again.

I had barely finished dinner, when Raq gave warning that someone was coming through the wood, and a moment later Tim ran up the caravan steps and, popping his head over the door, asked whether I thought it was a likely day.

" You can never be sure, of course," I said guardedly, opening the door; " but a warm shower, such as we had this morning, usually brings out all the beetles and worms from their hiding-places, and Hotchi knows this better than you and I do, so I shall be surprised if she goes on sleeping to-day."

Tim looked out of the window. " O' course, we can't mak' her come out. It's a case o' whether she's hungry or not. And if we went to her hole and pulled her out--"

" That wouldn't be wise, Tim. We should only frighten her. And besides, we want to watch her behaving naturally, so it is no use forcing her."

He looked a bit disappointed, then, brightening up, said, " If we don't see Hotchi, there's allus plenty of other things when I'm wi' you, Romany."

"That's the spirit! " I said heartily, and, seeing him casting wistful glances at my gooseberry tart, I said, " Help me to finish this up." He needed no second invitation, and between us we cleaned up the dish in a most businesslike manner.

" That ought to keep us going for the next few hours, I said, putting the greasy plates on the floor for Raq to lick while I washed up the cleaner ones.

Tim laughed as the dog nosed the plates about. " That's a fine way o' washin' up. He's nearly licked the pattern off that un. I'll dry 'em," said he, looking round for a cloth. Soon everything was tidy, so, putting Raq on the leash, for I did not want him to go ahead and hunt on his own, we sallied forth to where we thought Hotchi was still sleeping.

Arriving at the field, Tim looked anxiously about. " I can't see nothing of her, Romany, " he said disappointedly.

" Neither can I. Let's go quietly along the hedge side. We won't talk, and well put our feet down softly, and not clump about,"

Tim winked at me knowingly. "We'll do a bit o'stalkin', " he whispered.

" Hasn't the ground a lovely mossy smell after the rain?" I said. "So many people never notice it." Tim nodded.

We moved cautiously along the ditchside.

A blackbird flew along the side of the hedge, excitedly calling out,

"Chink-chink-chink." Tim made a wry face. "Noisy beggar!" he whispered.

"He would do that, just when we want to be quiet."

We walked right up the hedge side, but no Hotchi did we see.

" Let's get over this fence," I said; " she may be over in the other ditch." We had almost reached the bottom of the field when Raq leapt forward, pulling at his leash.

"He's smelt summat" said Tim, moving forward cautiously.

A few yards farther on he paused, and his face beamed with satisfaction as he pointed to the grasses moving this way and that.

" Grunt-snuffle-grunt,grunt-snuffle," and , standing still , we could just see the brown prickles of Hotchi as she shouldered her way towards the wood.

" She isn't half havin' a feed! " was Tim's comment.

A small dry wall, partially broken, separated the field from the wood. The hedgehog reached this, and started poking her nose in and out of the holes. From one of them she drew out a snail, and munched it with great satisfaction.

" Shell an' all! " whispered Tim with a grin. " That'll give her tummy-ache."

" It would take more than that to give her a pain, Tim. Why, I've seen one eat a dead bird without leaving a feather or a bone. Look ! She's starting to climb the wall."

We could hear her sharp nails scratching against the stones as she climbed, using every crack to prevent slipping. Her nose was turned this way and that in search for any trifle of food which came in her way.

" She seems to hunt without any kind of plan. She just goes where fancy leads. Look ! She's up on the top of the wall."

" I never knew a hedgehog could climb," Tim whispered.

" He can climb up most things. That's why it's difficult to keep a hedgehog in a garden. Trellis-work or wire is no problem to him. Look! She isn't finding anything to eat on the top of the wall, so she looks as though she's coming down."

" That'll tak' a bit of doin'. She'll need a step-ladder, I'm thinkin'."

"Watch carefully, I said. " Yes, she is coming."

Hotchi raised her head very slightly, for a hedgehog seldom looks upward. Her head fits so closely into her back that she seems to have no neck. Then, sniffing the air, she deliberately curled herself into a loose ball.

"She's goin' to sleep," said Tim. "Watch ! There ! Did you see that ?"

" Gosh, she fell off the wall on purpose !" said Tim excitedly.

" That's the quickest way to get down, isn't it, Tim?"

Quickly we went over to where Hotchi lay at the bottom of the wall, still rolled up. Then she relaxed, and her nose peeped out so cautiously that we could only just see its black nob.

" There may be an enemy about" I whispered, " so she's not taking any risks by opening right out at first."

" She's off now," said Tim. "Look! She's just sniffing about again as though she'd never had a fall. That's the rummiest way of gettin' down I've ever seen."

"I've seen one do the same trick after climbing a tree. You see, those prickles act as shock absorbers."

" What's them ? "

"Shock absorbers ? Oh, call them springs. You know the difference between a hard wooden chair and Father's easy-chair ? "

"Aye, by gum, I do! "Tim answered, rubbing himself at the thought of it.

" Well, that's how those prickles save Hotchi from getting hurt-she carries her springs about with her."

" And how did she come to think on it?" " Oh, that's a long story, but I'll tell you some day. It takes a bit of explaining."

A few minutes later Hotchi had apparently eaten all she wanted, for she suddenly turned round and made a bee-line for the hedge. As she disappeared Tim called out admiringly, " You're a knock-out, an' no mistake!"

A BADGER'S DEADLY WORK

It was a lovely afternoon, hot and sunny, and the ground had dried quickly after the rainfall of the night. Tim had come to see me, and was ready, I could see, for a ramble. Much to Rag's disgust, I locked him in the caravan, for no gamekeeper likes a dog to roam in and out of the hedges during May. There are too many partridges and pheasants either sitting on their nests or busy looking after their young broods.

" Shall we see anything of Hotchi asked Tim.

" We may do," I answered hopefully; " it is a very likely afternoon, isn't it? You remember, it was after a shower that she came out last time when we watched her climbing a wall. That reminds me, I want to show you what I found this morning."

We went deeper into the wood, until we got to a big beech tree. At the base of the tree lay a dead hedgehog.

"So that's the end of her," said Tim sadly. " We shan't be able to watch her any more, Romany."

"Oh, but that is not our Hotchi," I said ; " that's another one. This is a younger one." Tim turned it over with his foot, and gave an exclamation of surprise. " Gosh, there's nowt but its skin left ! Its innards have been cleaned out, same as an empty orange." He stooped and picked up the empty shell and examined it carefully.

" It's neatly done, isn't it? " I said. In answer to Tim's enquiring look, I continued, " That job was done by Brocky the Badger. Have you ever seen one, Tim?" He shook his head.

" That is because he only comes out at night when you are in bed. He generally leaves his burrow, or sett, as we call it, later than Hotchi does, as a rule, so it was just a bit of bad luck that he ran across this little chap."

" What's happened ? " asked Tim, still gazing at the empty skin.

" Oh, the hedgehog probably heard him coming along in the wood, so immediately rolled himself into a ball. Now, had his enemy been a cat, or even a fox, it would probably have passed him by and left him alone- that is, unless a fox was really hungry."

Tim put his fingers gently on the spines, still prickly, though there was no life within.

"I don't wonder they left him alone."

" But the badger rolled him over on his back, and just where the spines meet, he thrust in the claws of his two front paws. You ought to see a badger's claws to fully appreciate this, Tim. They are terrible weapons, long, and as hard as steel, and he uses them to dig with. Well, he pushed these well inside, and then prised it open. Then he probably chopped his head off with his strong teeth. The rest was easy. He munched away at his leisure, and it tasted so good that you can see he has licked the inside as clean as Raq licked those plates the other day."

" Poor little chap! " said Tim, putting the spiny shell on the ground. " But how do you know it isn't our Hotchi, Romany ? "

" If you look at this one, you'll notice that the spines are a nice warm brown colour. That shows that he isn't very old. Probably he was born last year. Now, our Hotchi has greyer-looking spines, which tell me that she may be three years old, or even more."

Tim gave a sigh of relief " Well, I am glad it isn't ours, anyway."

"So am I. As a matter of fact, if this dead one had only had a bit more sense, he might have been alive to-day."

Tim looked at me enquiringly.

" Sit down on this tree trunk for a minute, and I'll tell you what I mean. Hedgehogs, you see, Tim, have lived on this earth for thousands and thousands of years. If a race of animals can do this, it must have a way of outwitting its enemies, and also of outwitting other dangers. If not, the race dies out. What animal has died out ? " Here I paused, and looked hard at Tim for an answer.

He thought for a moment, and then said, " Wolf ? "

" Yes, the wolf in England will do, Tim. The only enemy the wolf couldn't overcome was man. If this island had been uninhabited, wolves might have been roaming about here still. Speed, savagery, hunting in packs, and cunning were the weapons by which they lived. Now, the hedgehogs adopted a different way of facing life. They grew spiny armour, and found that the best way to outwit most enemies was by curling up into a ball and lying still until the danger passed. This proved so successful that they never bothered to learn any other tricks. They didn't think it was necessary. Now do you understand what I mean? "

As Tim still looked doubtful, I said, " What does a rabbit do if you come across him in a field, Tim ?" He squats low," the boy answered promptly.

" What does he do then ? "

" Waits for the reet moment, and then scuttles for his burrer."

" That's right. You see, he not only knows how to freeze, "but also knows when to run for home." Tim nodded.

" But a hedgehog has only learnt one trick-to roll up and wait for some thing or nothing to happen. Rats , weasels , stoats , foxes, owls, hawks, cats, and most dogs usually leave him alone : his one trick pays him well. He learns it soon after he is born, and he uses it under every circumstance," I added with emphasis.

Tim nodded. " Aye, he does that."

" But last night, nosing about by that beech tree, he suddenly heard the sound of Brocky pushing noisily through the brushwood. Perhaps he knew what was making the noise. 'Anyhow,' he said to himself, ' I can always roll up. That will get me out of any tight comer.' So he curled up. You see, Tim, if he'd only had another trick, that of scuttling up the nearest hole, he might have been alive to-day. He is a chap with only one idea for every occasion, and last night it let him down. That's what I meant when I said he hadn't any sense."

" Aye, he's like our Bill. He thinks he's goin to make a good footballer because he can boot the ball up the field every time it comes near him." Here Tim picked up the empty skin and said, " You should have learnt to dribble your ball a bit, little feller."

" Good, Tim," I said. The boy flushed with pleasure at my praise.

" I suppose that's why we finds so many on 'em lyin ' dead on't roads killed by cars, isn't it ? " he asked.

" That is the best illustration you could have found," I said. "Here he is, nosing about on the high road, when suddenly he hears the rumble of a car. ' I'll curl up till the danger is over, ' he says , and the next morning you find his mangled body. A side-step on to the grass would have saved him."

Tim looked a bit depressed, I thought, so, to cheer him up, I said, " How about coming and having tea with me in the vardo? I dare say I can find something to eat."

He jumped up and gave a whoop of delight.

"We'll give all that's left of him a decent burial, shall we ? " I said.

So Tim dug a hole under a tree, and we left the chap of " one idea" in peace.

HOTCHI'S TIN HELMET

TIM had been helping me to collect firewood, and a fine heap we had gathered. Then we sat round the camp fire when dusk fell, and whilst the fire glowed, he asked me to tell him stories of the wild life in the fields. Just out of range of the flickering firelight stood the caravan, the windows reflecting the fire as a sudden flame leapt up. Overhead the branches of the trees looked like the great arms of an octopus stretching down their finger- tips to the warmth. The darkness deepened. " Hoo-hoo! Hooter-hoo! "' came from the recesses of the wood.

" The owd brown owl's wakin ' up," said Tim, nodding in the direction of the wood.

We sat in silence for a time, and I could see that Tim was busy thinking. Raq lay by my side curled up, sound asleep. Now and then, though still asleep, he gave little barks. Tim looked at me.

"Oh , " I said, laughing, " he's hunting for rabbits in his sleep. He sounds as though he is on the trail of one."

The next moment the silence of the night was broken by a long, muffled wail of pain. A loud clatter of noise came from somewhere near the vardo, tin-rattling and the sound of scattered dishes. Raq was alert in a second, and got up and barked. Tim looked scared and jumped up and followed me. We found that the row came from underneath the vardo.

"Bring one of those blazing sticks from the fire," I said; "then we can see what it is."

"By gum! " said Tim. " That's queer. It's an empty tin walkin' aboot on its own." Tim was right. The tin bobbed this way and that. Now it bumped against one of the wheels, now against a wooden box.

" What on-" Tim began.

Then we both of us laughed outright, for the light showed the tin stuck fast on the head of a hedgehog. The little chap couldn't see where he was going, and must have blundered first into one obstruction, then into another.

" He's got his muzzle on," said Tim with a grin.

I picked him up by a spine or two, and carried him to the firelight, and whilst Tim held the tin, I pulled his head carefully out. He then promptly rolled himself up into a ball, much to Tim's delight - Raq sniffed at him from a safe distance.

" Why, it's our Hotchi! " I said.

" How did she get it on her head? " asked Tim, as we settled ourselves by the fire with the hedgehog still rolled up before us.

" Well, you see, I had an empty tin, so I put some scraps of fat in it for the birds, and left it, together with a dirty pan or two, on the grass. Now, if there is one thing that Hotchl likes, it is a bit of fat. If I were to leave my frying-pan outside, I should get lots of hedgehog visitors. They can't resist a bit of fat or dripping. Hotchi must have been blundering along as usual by the hedge over there, when she suddenly smelt dripping. But unfortunately for her, the bottom of the tin was narrow, and the fat was at the bottom. So she pressed and pressed till she got her snout and head well in. But she forgot her spines, and so couldn't get her head out again. Then she got panicky and screamed."

" An' it were a scream an all, " said Tim. " It gave me cold shivers."

" Yes, it is rather a blood-curdling kind of sound, something like a hare's cry when she is in pain."

" So ye were playin' blind-man's buff, were you, Hotchie ? That'll teach ye not to be nosy."

" Not a bit of it," I replied; " she'll do the very same thing again to-morrow night if I leave any fat about."

Tim picked up the hedgehog carefully.

" I shouldn't handle her too much if I were you, Tim," I said. " You see, she is covered with tiny fleas."

" So she is' by gum ! " said Tim, dropping her rather suddenly. " She's wick wi' 'em. My, she has got some prickles ! I can't find a soft place anywhere. I wonder how many spines she's got?"

" I have heard it said by someone who took the trouble to count them, that hedgehogs have about twenty thousand, all told. Twenty thousand darts are not a bad protection from enemies, are they ? "

" And do they stick out like that when she walks about ? "

" Oh, no; she can raise them or keep them flat at will. By the way, Tim," I added, " can you move your ears ? "

Tim looked at me curiously. "Can I move me ears?" he repeated. "What do you mean, Romany?"

" I have met people who can waggle their scalps about. The skin on their head seems loose."

"Oh, I can do that. Look! " He raised his eyebrows, and I saw the top of his scalp move, and his ears slightly too.

" Yes," I said. " Good."

Tim pointed to the hedgehog. She was just beginning slowly to uncurl.

" Every human being, once upon a time, could do what you did. We all had muscles which could move our scalp and ears. Probably we could turn our ears forward or backward, as a horse does. But in most people their muscles have now become too limp to use. Yours, Tim, have a little more life in them than most folk's."

Tim nodded, and pointed at Hotchi. We could just see a black nose peeping out beneath a fringe of spines.

" Now, Hotchi," I went on, " has similar muscles on her back, and she uses them whenever she is frightened. That is how she can raise or lower her spines at will."

Seeing that she was not being interfered with, the hedgehog uncurled still further. Then she turned away from the fire, and shuffled into the wood, and we could hear her rustling through the undergrowth.

Come on," I said to Tim; " I think it is about time you were going home. We'll walk along together."

" I'm not afraid o' the dark, Romany. I can go by myself all right, thank ye."

" Oh , I know that, Tim. What is there to be afraid of ? Not a single animal or bird will attack you if you don't touch them. But I always like a walk in the woods at night. "

THE RIVALS

ALL morning thunder had rolled ominously. Then came a short, sharp storm with a deluge of rain, and after that the day had become brilliantly fine.

" Phew! But it were a nice drop o' rain, Romany."

" Quite a good shower," I said. " All the trees will have had their leaves nicely washed. Did you find it wet coming through the wood? " Tim shook his head.

" A bit moist-like in the shady places, but t' rest was dry. Can we go a walk ?" he asked eagerly.

" What do you say, Raq ? " I asked of the dog. Hearing the playfulness in my voice, he took it as a good omen, and pranced about.

"He's ready, anyway," Tim pleaded.

"Well, come and sit down until the grass really dries."

" Have ye had any more hedgehogs wandering round at nights? " asked the boy.

" I've not heard any. Of course, I've been careful not to leave my frying-pan about."

" I shall never forget the scream it gave when its head got stuck. Did ye say a hare makes a noise like that, Romany ? "

"Yes, when she gets caught in a snare. Sometimes I've heard it when a sportsman wounds her. It is a cry you don't want to hear twice, Tim."

"I don't want to hear Hotchi scream again."

Jim, the gamekeeper, tells me he often traps hedgehogs. He digs a hole in the ground, the shape of a pail upside down, and puts in some bait. One morning he had half a dozen of them. I asked what he did with them, and he laughed, and told me he gave them to old Martha Bell at the shop, and she boiled them."

" Does she eat 'em, Romany? " asked Tim. I laughed at the thought of old Martha munching away at boiled hedgehogs.

" No, I don't think she eats them, Tim, though I have eaten roasted hedgehogs, and jolly nice they are too. I rather think Martha boils them, scoops off the fat from the top of the water when it cools, and puts it into jars. Then when her knees are bad with rheumatism she rubs them with it. Some country people still think there is nothing better for this complaint."

The boy nodded. " Aye, Martha does hobble aboot, an' says pains is bad in 'er legs. But how do ye roast a hedgehog ? "

" There are two ways. One is to cover him with clay, and put him whole into the red ash of a fire. When cold, the clay breaks away, taking all the spines with it. But gipsies usually use a sharp knife, the knife they keep for making their clothes-pegs. They shave off the spines, slit the back right open, clean the inside out, put a spit through, and roast it over a red fire."

" I don't think I should like it," said Tim, making a face. .

Calling the dog to heel, we went our walk. Soon we came to the broken-down wall which we had seen Hotchi climb.

" I wonder if we shall see her again this afternoon, said Tim.

" It's quite likely. The grass is teeming with insect life, and have you noticed what a number of big slugs are about ? We shall have more rain to-night, I fancy."

" Aye, t' rabbits are oot feedin'. I've 'eard me father say that when they comes oot to feed in th' afternoon, it's 'cos they knows it's goin' to be wet at night."

" Wait a minute, Tim. Isn't that Hotchi, moving in those grasses? "

" Aye, it is; I can hear her sniffin'."

So once more we came across our little friend. She pushed her nose into a tuft of grass, and a big frog jumped out with a mighty jump.

"Near thing, that was," said Tim.

" Yes; another half-second, and it wouldn't have been a very pretty sight."

" What do you mean ? " he asked.

" Oh, a hedgehog is not a polite eater. That is what I mean. You see, he has a small mouth, and that means that he eats whatever he gets hold of, bit by bit. If he starts with a leg, he simply chews on and on from the leg until he gets to the body. You can see it is rather a nasty, messy business."

Hotchi had by this time shuffled on, but we soon found her. She was nosing about a ditch full of water. A big frog jumped plump into the ditch and disappeared. Hotchi pushed her nose well into the roots of grass from which the frog had appeared, and then looked at the water. The next moment she was swimming to the other side.

" Ee ! " said Tim. " I never knew a hedgehog could swim. Ye wouldn't think she had the legs to push hersel' along with, would you ?"

" Oh, she never minds a swim if there is anything to be gained by it. Look, she is still on the hunt for frogs." For a moment or two our attention was attracted from Hotchi to Raq. He had stopped at a rabbit hole and started to dig. His front paws were busy scraping out the earth, whilst his back legs kicked it out behind him. When I whistled him he looked round, but he was unrecognisable. His face was covered with soil, and the front part of his body was, as Tim said, " clarted up wi' muck." We could not help laughing at him. He looked such an object. I called him from his digging and put him into the ditch for a swim, and he paid us back for laughing at him and interrupting his sport, by coming out of the water and shaking himself as near to us as possible.

Farther up the field, in the bottom of the hedge, we heard once more grunts and groans. This time they were not normal sounds of quiet, pig-like satisfaction , but much fiercer.

" Come on, Tim! " I said, hurrying. "There's something going on there we ought to see."

I slipped the leash on to Raq , and cautiously but quickly we made our way to where the sounds came from.

Peeping in, Tim said excitedly, " There's two on them down there , Romany , as well as Hotchi , and they're having a rare old scrap."

It was true. There were two other hedgehogs, both facing each other defiantly. Each had the bristles immediately above their noses well forward. They made quick rushes at each other, and seemed to be trying to get underneath the rival's spines, as though searching for an unguarded place.

" What are they trying to do? " whispered Tim.

" I think they must be two Mr. Hedgehogs, boars, we call them. You know how two cockerels will fight each other for the mastery , or you've seen two bulls or rams meet in the same field? Well, that is what is happening here. They must have met by accident. Both were out hunting, and each is telling the other that there isn't room for both of them."

We watched their quick rushes, the swift uplifting of the mouth, as they tried to bite each other. Then I stepped in. They were so intent on fighting that they did not see me. One of them actually rushed over my feet in the savagery of his attack. When I lightly kicked him aside, he promptly turned into a ball. Tim jumped in, rolled the other fellow over, and he curled up. It was a funny sight to see the two heavyweights rolled up inert within a few inches of each other, their hate lost in the instinct for self-preservation. Tim laughed hilariously.

" Pick Hotchi up, Tim. We'll turn her loose over on the other side of the field, not far from her hole."

Tim, remembering what I had told him about the insect pests that infest a hedgehog, picked her up gingerly, put her in his red handkerchief, and took her over to the wall. When he returned, the other hedgehogs were shuffling to the hedge.

" Ye old prize-fighters," he said with a grin; " go an ' sleep off yer bad tempers."

We turned towards the vardo, and soon had the kettle singing merrily for a cup of tea.

THE FIGHT WITH THE ADDER.

TIM and I had quite a few walks during the next two weeks, but we never came across Hotchi. Perhaps she knew that the weather was too fine, and that it would be useless to wander about looking for food in hot sunshine. Then at last came a long-looked-for shower, which freshened up everything in the countryside, so we set out to see what we could find.

At the far end of the wall we picked up the trail of our friend again. As usual, she was busy hunting for slugs and beetles when we found her.

" Would she eat young birds if she came across them, Romany? "

"Oh, yes, and a day like this is a good one for coming across them. The grass is still very wet near the roots, and young birds flutter about and get their feathers so soaked that they can't rise. That is the hedgehog's chance."

We paused a moment to listen to Hotchi shuffling along.

"I say, Tim, what do you make that out to be ? " I said, pointing at something which lay in the sunshine just beneath a gorse bush.

" It looks like a twisted stick. No ! " he added excitedly; " it isn't, Romany. It's a snake ! "

" So it is, basking in the sunshine. There'll be some fun if the hedgehog runs into him, and if she keeps on in the same direction, she will. Keep perfectly still."

" What sort of a snake is it? " the boy whispered. " An adder, I think, by its dark colour. You see, it is only about a foot or so long."

" An adder? " he echoed, backing a few steps. "Then it'll poison our Hotchi, won't it ?"

"You'll see," I said. "Hotchi is well able to look after herself."

"I've only seen one afore, and that was up on t'moors. Me father says an adder 'as a V-mark just behind his 'ead, but he slithered away too quick fer me to see."

" Yes, you'll find them up there mostly. This chap has found out that there are plenty of frogs and lizards about here. So he comes where he can find his meals easily. Look, there's Hotchi coming out of the grass at the bottom of the wall. She is standing still, sniffing the air."

" Is she smelling the snake ? " said Tim.

" I think she may have got his scent. Raq has seen the hedgehog, too. Keep a tight hold on his collar, Tim. I shouldn't like the adder to bite him."

When Hotchl was about six feet from the snake, something must have warned the sleeper that danger was about, for he uncoiled slightly and flung out a coil of his body in front of his head, which was slightly raised. We could see his eyes glittering in the sunshine.

" Gosh, look at his sting dartin' in and out of his mouth ! " said Tim.

" That is his tongue, Tim, not his sting. The poison lies behind his teeth. Now watch ! " . As I spoke, the hedgehog rushed swiftly at the snake, and as she neared him pulled down her front spines over her face.

The snake struck at her nose with an angry hiss, then recoiled quickly as his own nose got the sharp pricks of Hotchi's bristles. Quick as lightning, Hotchi uncovered her head for a second, and before the snake could recover, she had seized it by the tail and curled herself up into a spiny ball. Again and again

65

the snake struck savagely at the prickly ball, each time wounding himself more severely. Hotchi remained curled up, holding on grimly to the tale, until the snake grew more and more feeble and lay exhausted. Then, and not till then, did Hotchi relax her hold.

" She's chewin' the snake's tail! " Tim whispered excitedly.

" She's going to make a meal of him," I said, as we watched the snake disappearing. When the hedgehog had eaten half of it, she paused, looked round, and shuffled off without giving another glance at the victim.

" She has had enough," I said. " She'll go back to her hole and have a good sleep. What with frogs, and half an adder, she must be about full up. "

When the hedgehog had disappeared, we walked over to the scene of the combat. I picked up the remains.

" Be careful, Romany," whispered Tim fearfully.

" It's all right, Tim. I wanted to show you the V plainly marked behind the head". We'll have a look at his mouth. " I prised it open with my knife, inserting a twig into the open jaws.

"What a big gape he has! " said Tim, not altogether comfortable at being so near.

"Can you see that his jaws are not locked together ? Look, the lower jaw can be pushed aside. That is to make room for swallowing large victims. Another thing, Tim. A snake has no eyelids. That lizard we once saw could move his eyelids, couldn't he? "

" Where is the poison, Romany? " Tim asked, still standing a few feet away.

"See those two fangs about a third of an inch long in the upper jaw? When he is not using them, they lie flat against the palate-the top of the mouth, you know."

"I see em, " he whispered.

" Somewhere behind these the poison lies, two channels connecting it with each fang. As soon as the adder saw that he had to fight Hotchi, he raised those two fangs. Look, they are as sharp as needles, aren't they ? When he struck, the poison would run down the channels to the fangs. Had Hotchi been a rabbit, of course, she would soon have been done for. But though an adder's bite sometimes kills human beings, it has no effect on a hedgehog. He is what we call 'immune,' Tim."

" Ugh ! " said the boy, shivering a little. " I don't like snakes. What would ye do if one was to bite me, Romany? "

" Suck the wound and spit it out," I replied. "Then tie a bandage above the bite as tight as you could bear it, get some Condy's Fluid from somewhere and bathe it, and then make you lie down quietly whilst I sent for a doctor."

" And what should I feel like?

" Probably a bit giddy and faint."

" And would I git better? "

" Oh, yes, after a week or so. But don't bother your head about snakes. Leave them alone, and they will be only too glad to leave you alone. Though you don't like them, they help farmers a good deal by eating up insect pests. I should never kill a snake myself unless I was forced to."

We buried the snake's head before we made our way back to the vardo. Tim had had enough for one day !

THE HEDGEHOG FAMILY

"WELL," said Tim, as we sat on the vardo steps after tea, " I know a deal more about hedgehogs than I did afore you came, Romany."

" You do, Tim, " I replied, " and it is not hearsay evidence, either. You have seen things with your own eyes, and that is the best way to learn." I paused for a moment. " I found something else this morning which will interest you, or, rather, Raq found it, didn't you, old man ? "

Tim looked up eagerly and enquiringly, and Raq wagged his stump of a tail nearly off.

"We found," I went on, "Hotchi's nest."

"With young uns in it ?" Tim asked excitedly.

"Yes, but how many, I don't know. I didn't touch it."

Can we go and look at it, Romany? " he pleaded, at the same time giving Raq a pat for finding it.

" If we do-and this isn't the right time to go-you, old man," I said to the dog, " will have to be left behind, I'm afraid."

" Why shouldn't we go now ? " Tim asked impatiently.

" Oh, it's better to wait till dusk. Then perhaps Mother Hotchi will go out to find food, and we'll have a chance to look at her youngsters."

So as the shadows deepened, Tim and I set out for the field we now knew so well. Tim started running towards the hole in which the hedgehog always liked to sleep, but I called him back.

" She's not there, Tim, but across in the opposite hedge." We walked across the field very quietly.

We paused in front of a tree whose roots spread out far beyond the hedge into the field. Between two of these roots was a small hole. I got my torch out and flashed a light on it.

"In there," I said.

"How ever can a hedgehog get through that small hole ? " asked Tim excitedly. " Why, it would tak' a rabbit all its time to push through. "

" It wouldn't do for her to choose one with a wide entrance, would it ? Any enemy could get in too easily. Get down and have a good look at it.

But don't touch it with your hands. " Tim peered in.

" I can't see inside. There's leaves blocking it. Can't I put my hand in, Romany ? I do want to see the little uns."

" Perhaps I had better do it," I replied; " I've brought an old pair of gloves for the job."

"Gloves ? Are ye frightened o' gettin' yer hands scratched? " asked Tim. I shook my head.

" You know I have always told you what a keen nose a hedgehog has. If I handled those baby hedgehogs, when she comes back, she will smell that some human being has found them. And then-well, all might not be well for those youngsters."

"Why, what would 'appen? " asked Tim.

"She might eat them."

"Eat 'em?" said Tim disgustedly. "Whatever for ?"

" To put them out of harm's way. She would be so fearful for them lest any harm should befall them. Many animals do that-rabbits, for instance."

" Aye, we had a young sow once as ate her young uns. I never knew afore why."

I got down on my knees. Then I worked my fingers carefully through the leaves, and finally felt the young hedgehogs, lying as warm as toast.

" I heerd 'em squeak! " said Tim excitedly.

Very carefully I brought one little chap out in my palms.

" Why, he's no spines on 'im! " said Tim wonderingly. "He's only got white silky hairs."

" Yes, that's so. Those hairs will grow into spines in a week or two.

It wouldn't do for them to be born with prickles , would it ? A nest full of pin-cushions wouldn't sleep very comfortably together, would they? "

"And how does Hotchl feed 'em? " asked Tim.

"Just as a cat feeds her kittens, Tim. There again, if those silky hairs

were spines, the mother wouldn't have much peace, would she? "

"The little beggar is sound asleep, Romany."

" You mean he has got his eyes shut. He may be asleep, but actually he is born blind, just like puppies are. Now, I think he has been out in the open long enough."

So I put the little fellow back with his brothers and sisters and left the hole just as we had found it.

" And what's Mr. Hotchi doin'? " asked Tim." Doesn't he help to look after his babies? "

" I don't think so. He leaves it all to his wife , and has an easy time on his own."

We did not touch the nest again, but stood a moment listening, and , hearing the squeaking inside, we knew that our visit had not harmed them.

As evening fell we passed a cock pheasant perched in a tree.

" Another father who neglects his family," I said.

Tim nodded. "Now I come to think on't, I've niver seen 'im out wi' 'is missus an' kids."

A couple of weeks later Tim and I came across the hedgehogs again.

They were all out together. And what a shuffling there was as they searched for food !

"They've got their spines all right now," said Tim.

" Yes, Hotchi won't risk taking them out until they have their weapons and armour ready."

As we came near, Hotchi and all the family immediately curled up into balls, and lay quite still. It was a comical sight to see the lot of them with their bristles up.

" You see, she has taught them already what to do, Tim. I dare say when she saw us she called out, 'Roll up -roll up-danger!' and immediately they obeyed her.

We walked a short distance from them, and then waited to see them uncurl. Tim would have stayed there all day, so fascinated was he, but they disappeared into the bottom of the hedge. That was the first and last time we saw them all out together.

SHE PREPARES FOR WINTER.

SUMMER, had turned to autumn before I visited the farm with my caravan again. The woods were fast losing their leaves, and sharp frosts were whitening the fields.

" And have you seen anything of Hotchi? " I asked Tim when he came to see me the first night I arrived.

"Oh, aye, a few times. She were busy, as usual, pokin' her nose aboot lookin' for what she could find. One day I saw her eatin' a young rabbit caught in a snare. But I haven't seen her lately."

After we had had something to eat, Tim, Raq, and I set off for a walk. Even though the wind was in the east, Raq went in and out of the stream as though it were summer. I made Tim feel the dog's skin, and he was surprised to find that he was only wet on top. His skin underneath was dry and warm.

For a time we saw no signs of Hotchi, and thought we were going to be disappointed, but as the afternoon waned we saw something moving on the top of a bank where once a hedge had grown.

" There she is! " said Tim. " Isn't she a fat un?"

I hastily called Raq to heel and put him on the leash. The hedgehog truly did look fit and well, though not perhaps quite as active as in the summer time. She seemed to walk a trifle more heavily, and her nose was not probing into every hollow and tuft of grass.

" Yes, she is fat. If you could look under her skin you would find a thick layer of it. Everything she has eaten lately has gone to the making of it." The boy looked at me enquiringly.

" You know, of course, that she always goes to sleep during the winter , don't you?" Tim nodded. "Aye."

"That's her way of facing the winter, like the dormouse and the squirrel. Swallows and hosts of other birds fly south for the winter, some to Africa and some to southern Europe, but Hotchi prefers to stay here. She couldn't exist, though, if she tried to live as she does in summer. When anything is using up energy, it needs a lot of food to nourish it. But if it lies in bed quietly, it can eat much less. So Hotchi lays up a store of fat under her skin, then goes to sleep, and that fat lasts her all the winter and keeps her engine of life just ticking over. Do you remember the name of another animal that can store up food in his body ? Not an English animal."

Tim thought for a moment. " I know-a camel."

As he spoke, the hedgehog rolled herself into a ball, and, whether by accident or design, rolled down into the ditch a few feet below us.

" We saw her do that trick once afore," said Tim. " We did, but look at her unrolling now."

" Oh! " said Tim. " She's got a lot o' dry leaves stuck on her spines, and look, she's climbing up the bank again! "

Up went the hedgehog to the top, the leaves still sticking on her spines. She walked heavily along for some yards, then curled herself into a ball once more and rolled down again, getting up with more leaves impaled.

" She is havin' a game, and no mistake! " said Tim.

"She'll have a job to get them leaves off."

" I don't think she will want to get them off. You see, that is her way of making an overcoat for the winter. Not much draught can get through that covering."

Tim whistled. " I never thought of that. What a good wheeze! I wonder how she found it out? "

" Oh, by accident, I should think, in the first place. Look, she's off now. Doesn't she look a queer object with all those leaves stuck on her ? Some people say that she goes into orchards, and deliberately rolls on apples, and carries them off to her hole. And so gardeners kill hedgehogs because they think they steal apples."

Tim scratched his head. " I should tell 'em I've never seen a hedgehog eat anything 'cept slugs, frogs, and beetles, and, oh, adders! "

" You're right, Tim. A hedgehog is a flesh-eater, not a vegetable-eater. Look, she has come down from the bank, and is walking along the ditch now."

69

" But where are her youngsters, Romany ?"

" Gone out into the world to find their fortunes, Tim. She only looks after them for about six weeks. She may even have had another litter since those you and I saw."

A little farther on Hotchi paused in front of a hole at the root of a tree. Then she squeezed herself through.

"That is where I think she will stay for the winter, " I whispered.

" You don't think we shall see her again, Romany ?"

I shook my head. " I hardly think so, Tim. The weather is turning so cold. She will carry into that hole heaps of dry leaves and moss and litter of all sorts, and she will see that the entrance door is well blocked. Then if we could watch her, we should see her crawl right into the centre of this mass of leaves, looking very sleepy. Then she will begin to curl herself up, withdrawing her nose so that the soft hair on the under parts of her body covers it. She will tuck her little feet inside too, and then forget everything in a deep sleep until next March."

" Won't she wake up afore that ? "

" Yes, I have found hedgehogs shuffling about in winter. Perhaps in a spell of mild weather she may come out of her hole for a few hours to find a bit of food. But she soon goes back and wraps herself up again in her bed. So we will leave her in peace, shall we? "

I thought Tim looked a little regretfully at Hotchi's hiding- place, as though sorry to part with an old friend.

" I'll tell you what you can do Tim. If you come this way in the winter sometimes, if you listen carefully, you will probably hear her snoring. Then you will know that our little friend is alive all right."

" I will, Romany, and then I'll tell you when you come this way again. Shall we see her again next Spring?"

" Yes, we may; but there are such a lot of other animals and birds as interesting to watch. What about watching a fox some time, Tim ? "

The boy's eyes glistened.

" That would be fine ! You'll be moving off in your caravan agin in t' mornin', won't you, Romany? Ee, I shall miss our walks together."

BILLY THE SQUIRREL.

TREE-TOP HIGHWAYS

IN May a new voice was to be heard echoing in the wood and rolling down the glen : the cuckoo had arrived.

"Spring is surely here," I said to Raq, as he sunned himself on the vardo step, gazing idly at birds that flitted past. A low growl told me that a visitor was coming. It was Tim, with my morning's milk.

" Heard the cuckoo, Romany? " he asked.

" Yes-we shall hear it wherever we go, for a month or two."

As we came out of the vardo door we caught sight of the bird.

" It is like a sparrow hawk, isn't it, Tim ?" I said, as the bird alighted, stooped forward and sent out its call.

" I'd like to find its nest . . . I mean a nest where it lays its egg," he corrected himself quickly.

" That bird will never lay an egg," I laughed, " that's the cock- bird who has come on in advance. Mrs. Cuckoo won't arrive from Africa for a week or more."

" Then why is he calling out like that, if he's alone ?

" So that when Mrs. Cuckoo does arrive she'll hear him, and know there's a mate waiting for her." The bird flew over the hedge.

" Aye, you're right, Romany, it is like a hawk."

" Yes, but only in appearance. The cuckoo doesn't hunt anything, except those hairy caterpillars on which he thrives. I expect his hawk-like appearance protects him. Other birds fear him a bit."

As we were fetching a pail of water from the brook I showed Tim a small bee-like fly that hovered near the hedge. It flew either backwards or forwards with equal ease.

"You might mistake that little fellow for a wasp," I said.

He nodded.

"He's got a yellow body, but he's smaller than a wasp. Does he sting? "

"No. He copies the cuckoo. He dresses like a wasp so that birds will let him alone. Those yellow stripes are danger-signals. "Let me alone! I'm dangerous!' they say.

On our way back we passed a clump of what looked like nettles, by the side of the hedge.

" Get me a handful of those nettles, will you ,Tim ? It's quite all right," I said, laughing , " you've only to say Abracadabra,' and they won't hurt you."

Very gingerly Tim put his hand amongst the fronds." Stinging ?"I asked.

I could see by the surprise on his face that he felt nothing.

"Those are dead nettles-plants which imitate the stinging nettle's appearance to keep cattle from browsing on them. Keep clear of me! ' the leaves say, ' I sting.' "

" Gosh! said Tim. " They're a good imitation,' an' all."

When my buckets were well filled, and Raq had finished his breakfast Tim said :

" I suppose we've seen the last o' them otters, Romany ? "

" I think so. They shifted to another holt, you know, as soon as the hunt had gone by."

He was silent for a moment.

" Could we watch your squirrel a bit, Romany? " he asked.

" Of course. Billy used to be allowed to come in here at one time. But I had to turn him out, because he made such a mess of the vardo."

"How did you 'tice him inside?"

I used to watch him jumping about in that fir tree across the lane. I left crumbs out on the ground for him, but Raq used to chase him away. Then I slung some peanuts outside the window, and the rest was easy."

"Did he break your cups and things, Romany? "

"Not at first. He used to clamber round the vardo on the inside beams, leaving his claw-marks on the paint. Then, one morning, two of them came in. They quarrelled over a piece of Madeira cake, and ended by scattering my plates and cups on the floor. When Raq joined in , there was a fine shimozzle. So I discouraged them from coming inside again."

Tim grinned. " I should like to have been 'ere."

" Yes. Let's go out into the wood and see if we can find him."

The sun was shining in all its glory as Tim, Raq and I set out. The air was balmy, and the hawthorn buds on the hedges were eager to open. Everywhere birds were singing. The woods rang with the falling cadence of the willow warblers; chaffinches "pinked," wrens rattled their alarms at our approach, and far above us the larks sprayed their territories with challenging music.

We wandered about in the wood for some time. Then I heard a familiar sound, and caught sight of a flash of red fur amongst the opening buds above us.

" There's Billy," I said. " Come and sit behind this bush and see if he will come down."

From branch to branch the little fellow sprang, pausing only to stare inquisitively down at us, with his head on one side.

" He seems to know his way about," said Tim.

" Squirrels know the tree-tops as well as we know our lanes and paths. If we could follow Billy on his journeys, we should find that he always travels along certain routes. He knows where the branches of trees intertwine, making bridges. He knows to an inch how far he has to jump from one tree to another-and he always goes along the same way. He teaches his family, too, the routes he has learned."

Tim nodded. " He's coming down yon fir tree head first, like the nuthatch does. He's flattened himself against the trunk, Romany."

I handed Tim my field-glasses. " Can you see him better with these ? Look at his feet."

Tim took some time adjusting the glasses to his sight.

"My, what claws ! Five on his hind-feet and four on his front 'uns. And look at them long nails. No wonder he can hang on to owt."

" See his ears, Tim? " I said.

" I don't see much wrong with them neither."

" But what has he on them that no other animal has ? "

" Oh, aye, tufts on the tips of his ears. I never noticed that afore."

" And he is the only animal we have whose ears are covered with hair. The tufts begin to grow very thick now, and again in winter. Queer, aren't they? I always recognise Billy because one of his tufts is thicker than the other."

" Aye, so it is, Romany," said Tim, handing me back the glasses.

Billy came down the tree at a great speed and ran across the path in front of us.

" Graceful up aloft but very ungainly on the ground," I said, as we watched him running with his tail stretched out straight behind him. " His front legs seem to be too wide apart."

Then I think Raq must have moved in some way that alarmed the little chap, for he scampered to the nearest tree and disappeared.

"Where has he gone ? " asked Tim, as we emerged from our hiding- places.

" Not as far away as you think."

He looked at me enquiringly.

" Walk past the tree, and you'll see."

Tim did so, and laughed.

" He was only a yard from the ground on t'other side of the trunk."

" Yes, it's one of his favourite tricks. He stays near the ground, knowing that we shall look upwards for him."

Discovered, the squirrel shot up the trunk into a safe fork.

"Vut-vut-vut," he cried angrily.

"He's scolding us, Romany, isn't he?

"Yes," I said. " He and the wren seem to use more bad language than any other birds and animals. But he is really a very friendly little fellow. It is a pity we have got nothing in our pockets to offer him."

" Would he come down, d' you think? " asked Tim.

" If I know Billy," I answered laughingly, "he would follow us all the way to the vardo for the smell of a peanut. But without some kind of offering you'll never get him to come down."

And so it proved. For that morning, at any rate, we had to be content with Billy scolding us from a distance.

NEXT-DOOR NEIGHBOURS

" WHAT'S yon bird, Romany ? "

Tim and I were crossing the bleak upland fields where the plovers love to build their nests. No sooner had we escaped their excited attentions, than a brown and white bird attached itself to us, circling overhead with a persistence that provoked Tim's curiosity. Its wing-beats were not steady like those of a wood pigeon or rook, but convulsive and irregular, so that it rose and dipped alternately in its flight.

" It's a red shank," I answered Tim. " You can see the colour of its long legs from here."

" Pu-ee, pu-ee," came the bird's plaintive cry as he skimmed the grey stone wall ahead of us, and dropped out of sight.

" It seems worried over summat," said Tim. " Has it got a family somewhere near, d' you think ?"

" Not a family, yet, " I answered. " But we may find a nest if we search long enough."

We climbed the rough stone wall, and after hauling Raq over by the scruff of his neck, I gave him an encouraging pat and told him to see what he could find. Meanwhile, Tim and I took up our places a dozen yards apart, and began to cross and re-cross the field, keeping our eyes on the ground. Suddenly Tim gave a cry which startled me, and leaped backwards so quickly that I ran to him , thinking he had hurt himself.

" What is it, Tim ? An adder ? "

Tim said nothing, but pointed to the ground with such a comical expression of dismay on his puckered face, that when I saw what the trouble was, I could not help laughing. In a slight depression lay an oozing, yellow mess. He had stepped on a nest of eggs.

" I never saw a thing 'til my foot was on it and the eggs went crunch," he said apologetically. " You're not angry, are you, Romany ?"

" No, of course not," I reassured him, smiling. " You're not by any means the first person who has trodden on a red shank's nest. It is so well camouflaged that you can easily make a mistake-just as you can when looking for plovers' eggs. And, by Jove!" I broke off suddenly, and bent down to examine the remains of the nest, " I believe they are plovers' eggs, Tim! There's not much difference between a plover's and a red shank's eggs, except in shape-and you haven't left much shape in this lot for me to judge by! But I've never seen a red shank's nest as bare as this one-they usually line it with a few straws or something. But this is just the sort of hollow the plover makes. . . . Let's look again, and see if we can't find the red shank's nest after all."

Our search was soon ended. While we had been examining one nest, Raq had sniffed out another not ten paces away.

" Well, that lets me out! " said Tim cheerfully, when I told him that this was indeed the red shank's nest. " I'm glad it was only plovers' eggs I broke. Fancy them red shanks making a nest so close ! Do the mother-birds like company when they're hatching out their eggs, Romany ?"

" I don't know," I said, laughing. " It's a very curious thing that the two birds should nest so near each other, when they've got the whole field to lay their eggs in. But I've noticed the same thing before. It is fun to imagine the mother-birds sitting gossiping about the future of their babies, discussing whether they are going to make them soldiers or sailors, but I'm afraid that is only an amusing fairy-tale. I think, all the same, that the red shank deliberately chooses to be near the plover for protection. You know the way the plover behaves when he sees us coming into his field ? "

" Aye, he treats us like burglars," said Tim.

" Yes, the cock-plover is always on guard. No carrion crow, or any other marauder for that matter, can come into the field without being harassed by the plover. So the red shank settles nearby, relying on his policeman friend to keep burglars away."

On the way home we sauntered into the wood.

" We may see Billy again," said Tim, and we had not walked many yards before I saw something move near the top of a pine tree.

" You're a good prophet, Tim," I said, pointing upwards.

There, on the side of a wood pigeon's nest, sat Billy, He seemed to be holding something between his paws, but we could not be sure of this, so I got out my field glasses.

" The wicked little beggar is eating either the wood pigeon's eggs, or the young birds in the nest," I said.

Tim took the glasses, adjusted them to his sight, and said "Gosh ! So he is, Romany. He's got an egg in his paws."

We waited until the red thief left the nest. Then he ran along his aerial highway, and, perching on a branch where he thought himself screened from view, began to lick himself clean.

" He is licking off blood-marks, I said. " Tell your father, Tim, that Billy has been thinning out his wood pigeons. He will be very pleased."

" I never knew a squirrel did that, Romany."

" All squirrels don't," I said. " Usually the only crime they commit is to ruin young trees by stripping them of their bark. Some of them like birds' eggs, especially those of the wood pigeon. I don't think they actually search for them, but as they pass along the tree- tops they often catch sight of the eggs, which are chalk-white. And a squirrel is a very inquisitive animal."

Farther on we caught sight of Billy and another red squirrel taking flying leaps after one another in the treetops. It made us quite dizzy to watch the risks they took as they sprang from branch to branch.

" Those two are going to make a nest."

" That isn't what you called it before," said Tim quickly.

" No. A ' drey ' was what I called it. It looks as though Billy will soon have a family to look after. Perhaps we can find the nest, or ' drey" that he has built for them."

For a hundred yards we marched along the path like Johnny-Head-in- Air, bumping into one another and falling over Raq as we did so. Once, Tim called my attention to-a mass of twigs lodged high up in a tree- fork, but this, I told him, was a magpie's nest, and not what we were looking for. Then, suddenly, we came upon three dreys-domes of sticks with an entrance at the side-built in three trees not far from one another. One was in the top of a big hawthorn tree, another in a holly bush, and the third wedged up against the trunk of a sycamore. This last one seemed to be the easiest to get at, so I made a " back " for Tim, and he pulled himself up on a long, swaying branch. From there he worked his way along to the trunk of the tree, and soon climbed to the nest itself.

" It's made of twigs with moss and leaves," he shouted," but there's nowt in it yet."

Once on the ground again, he wanted to try to reach the other nests, but I told him that I thought it a waste of time.

" If there is nothing in that nest next time we come," I said, " you can have a shot at climbing the other trees."

" We shall know better then which drey belongs to Billy, shan't we? " said Tim, dusting his knees and trousers.

" Oh, I think they all belong to Billy," I said. " Squirrels make two or three dreys, just as wrens make two or three nests in the same season. The question is: Which one is he going to rear his family in?"

" I'll have to keep watching them nests."

" Yes. When you're sure that you know which one Billy has chosen, come and tell me, won't you?"

" You bet I will! " were his last words, as he disappeared through the gate leading to the farm.

A "MANX" SQUIRREL

" HOW good a pipe tastes on a morning like this, " I said to Raq. I was sitting contentedly on the stile near the vardo, enjoying the luxury of being thoroughly lazy. Rag sniffed at the pipe and then drew back his head in disgust. The look he gave me as he licked his nose suggested that I had played a trick on him.

I sat and watched the yellow bees sweeping from one flower to another. The heavy bumble bees, too, were industriously collecting pollen-like stout market-women weighed down with their purchases. And the way in which their buzzing note took on a deeper tone when two of them met in mid-air-as though exchanging morning courtesies-lent colour to my fancy.

A robin flitted down to snatch up a crumb or two from the worn patch of grass in front of the caravan. From a nearby branch he sang his little song of thanks-a well known refrain, whose delicate phrasings and rippling trills finished on a single drawn-out, plaintive note. A blackbird succeeded him. For a moment he scraped diligently among the dead leaves at the hedge-side. Then he mounted to the vardo roof and gave out half a dozen mellow, disconnected notes, as though tuning up for a finer performance when he found a more appreciative audience. The sound of Tim's footsteps in the lane scared him, and he sped away with flirting wings.

"Chink-chink! " he called indignantly.

Opening the basket he carried, Tim displayed twelve brown eggs, a loaf, and a small jar of lemon-cheese.

" I'll make some sandwiches with that, Tim, while you go down to the brook and pick some water-cress, will you ?"

Nothing loath, Tim whistled to Rag and off they went to where the stream widens to form a pool. As I cut the top off the loaf, I watched the two of them through the vardo window, and saw that Raq was nosing about eagerly among the long grasses at the water's edge.

" Raq thought you said water-hen not water-cress," said Tim, when he returned. " And he's half soaked me with his splashing."

" Have you found which drey Billy has decided to use ? " I asked, when we had filled our pockets with sandwiches.

" Yes, it's the one in the holly bush," said Tim. Then showing me a red weal on his arm, he said, not without a touch of pride:" I got this trying to climb up to it."

"Did you reach the drey ?"

"Not quite," was his rueful answer. " A branch broke and I came down quicker nor I went up, but it's the right drey, I know, co's I've seen Billy and his missus hopping in and out of it."

By this time we were nearing the place where the dreys were, and keeping a sharp lookout for Billy.

" There he is ! " I exclaimed, as a flash of red caught my eye.

"Behind that fallen trunk."

But I was mistaken. The squirrel which ran along the path in front of us was not Billy. In fact, for a moment I was almost prepared to believe Tim's cry: "It's a weasel ! "

"No," I said, focusing my glasses on the little creature as he darted up a tree-trunk. " it's a squirrel right,enough, but he has lost his tail."

" Oh, the poor thing! How did he do that, Romany ?"

" He may have been caught in a trap. A squirrel's tail isn't very strong, you know, and a trap might chop it off short like that. Or he may have lost it at the river."

"The river ? " queried Tim.

" Yes. You know where the stepping-stones are; haven't you ever seen squirrels tripping across them ? "

"Can't say I have. " said Tim.

"Well, you can take it from me that they do cross from one side to the other, jumping from stone to stone with their tails stretched out behind them. And then along comes a big pike and . . ." I brought my hands together with a snapping movement, " Off with his tail. In fact, the squirrel can think himself lucky if it's not 'off with his head ! ' "

" Would a pike go for a squirrel ?"

"He will' go for anything in or on the water that's alive. He's particularly fond of young duck-lings. I believe he'd swallow young rabbits, too, it he could only get out and chase them."

Tim grinned. "What'll happen to yon squirrel with no tail ? "

" He won't live long, I'm afraid. You saw how clumsy he was compared with Billy, and how nearly he missed his jump to that second branch up there. One of his enemies will get hold of him before long."

" What is his worst enemy, Romany? " ,

"Oh, the pine-marten, undoubtedly. Fortunately for Billy and his kind, however, there are not many of them left now."

" Have you seen many, Romany ?"

" I have only seen two, though at one time they were to be found in all our woods. They are the weasels of the trees, you know."

" There seem to be all sorts of weasels, Romany," was his comment.

" Yes, the otter, stoat and pine-marten are all cousins. The otters chose to live in the water, and the weasels and stoats remained on the ground, but the pine-martens took to the tree-tops."

" What's he like ? "

" Oh, bigger than the stoat-twice as big, with lovely rich brown fur and a creamy-white breast. He's an expert climber, of course."

" Better than Billy ? "

" He can leave Billy standing. He's the quickest thing on four feet in the trees. A squirrel has only one chance of escape when the marten is after him, and that is to keep to the slender branches where his enemy dare not follow. A pine-marten can run up and down the trunk of a tree like greased lightening."

" And why is there none about nowadays ? "

" They have been trapped and shot at so much that now they are only found where there are no men-in the fastness of Wales and Cumberland."

Tim thought this over, holding on to a slender branch meanwhile, to prevent it whipping back at me as I followed him.

" Will owls and hawks go for Billy? " he asked.

It was my turn to reflect.

"I don't think owls will bother him much," I said slowly. "You see, Billy is one of those creatures who is not afraid of daylight. He goes to bed, too, at a decent hour, and so the owl doesn't see much of him, though I dare say the short-eared owl which hunts by day might try and catch him unawares. But really, he's rather too big for a hawk or an owl to tackle. I once saw a merlin stoop at a squirrel, but I think that was exceptional."

" I expect that's why most folks have seen squirrels, but not otters or badgers," said Tim. " Because they come out in the day-time, I mean," he added.   At that moment Billy obliged us by announcing his presence. A thin shaving of bark came floating down through the branches above us, and looking up we saw his bright eyes peering out from a crevice in the tree.

" Have you got those peanuts yet?

Tim shook his head. " There's none in the shop , " he said regretfully. " But I asked Martha to get me some for this week."

" Well, we'll see if bread will tempt him."

I broke off a comer of one of my sandwiches, and scattered a few crumbs on the ground for Billy to see. Then I held out my hand, and called to the little fellow to come. But Billy was both wary and temperamental. Even when I left the bread on the path, and retired to where Tim was crouching, keeping Raq in check, it was some moments before he would venture to the ground.

" He doesn't know it's you, Romany," said Tim.

" No," I agreed, " not at this distance from the vardo. You can't expect him to, really. He certainly used to come to the vardo when I was there, but only after days of reconnoitring and hesitation. When he had satisfied himself that there was absolutely no danger, and that Raq wouldn't hurt him , he ventured inside, and I soon had him eating out of my hand. But away from the vardo, he was always more cautious. All two-legged things must look very much alike from the tree-tops, just as all cities look the same from an aeroplane, and Billy doesn't connect me with the vardo yet."

The squirrel nibbled at the piece of bread I had left for him, and then dropped it a trifle disdainfully. For a second he eyed us appraisingly, so that I thought his curiosity was getting the better of his caution, and that he would come and examine my pockets as of old. But after advancing a few steps towards us with his nose quivering to catch our scent, he suddenly took fright.

" Now watch his tail," I said, as he flashed up the trunk of a tree. " You'll soon see what that other squirrel has lost. He uses it, too, as a blanket which he can wrap round himself when he goes to sleep, like the fox does. And he has lost a parachute as well."

With every turn and twist that Billy made as he climbed and dived alternately, his fine bushy tail jerked out to balance him.

" He kind of spreads himself when he's jumping, don't he, Romany ?"   " Yes," I agreed. " He seems to launch himself on to the air as though it were as substantial as water. In fact, I think he travels quicker when he is running along a branch, than when he is actually in the middle of a jump."

"He's summat like a paper-dart-the way he floats," said Tim, as Billy disappeared from view, and we continued our walk. "Did you ever make one of them things when you was at school , Romany?"

" I did, Tim," I laughed, " and I dipped them in the inkwell, too, before throwing them."

Tim grinned : " We used the jam off our bread at school yesterday," he said reminiscently.

A PERILOUS "FLITTING"

ON one of my walks a few days later, I met Jim, the gamekeeper. Tim was not with me because he was at school. The heavy, double- barrelled gun which the keeper carried in the crook of his left arm glittered in the fitful sunshine. The triggers were cocked ready for action, and I respected the meticulous care with which he avoided pointing the gun in my direction, even when he turned to fall into step with me.

Jim does not waste his words, and after exchanging greetings we walked between the young fir trees for half a mile or so in companionable silence. Then, up went Jim's arm, and the noise of his gun echoed down the broad, straight ride.

" That's another o' them -American visitors gone to where he belongs," he said with satisfaction, as Raq ran to retrieve the little animal that had dropped out of one of the fir trees.

" A grey squirrel," I said, as Raq laid the unhappy object at my feet. " He doesn't look like a villain, does he? "

" Mebbe not," agreed Jim, "but he's one of the worst pests we have, fer all that. I'm agoin' to stick him up on my gibbet, and I'll hope to see all 'is relations alongside of him afore long."

"Not Billy," I said anxiously." You're not out for the red squirrel's blood, too, are you ? "

" No, only the grey," he reassured me' "And I'll be doing your friend Billy a favour, an' all."

" Yes, I believe you will, Jim. If these foreigners go on multiplying as they are doing at present, there won't be a native red squirrel left in the whole country before very long. They're killing, off our red squirrels somehow or other, though I don t quite, know how they do it. Does the grey squirrel go for Billy and his like with teeth and claw, or does he just-starve him out? Perhaps you know, Jim? "

The keeper considered a moment before answering.

" There's a kind of a war goin' on between the red squirrels and these foreigners," he said slowly, " but 'ow far they carry it, I don't rightly know."

" You mean you don't think they go for each other whenever they meet ? " I queried.

" No," Jim shook his head. " They quarrel over food, mebbe, or a love affair, or summat. Besides, the red 'ud never go for the grey. It'd be suicide." "So it's a massacre rather than a war" I suggested.

"When they do fight-yes," agreed Jim. "The foreigner is bigger and stronger nor Billy, and 'e has the advantage all the time. 'E finds where Billy's stores of food are and raids them-that's when 'e's most likely to set on Billy hisself. And 'e can fit hisself to conditions all over the country better nor the red squirrel," he continued. " That's why no amount of trappin' and shootin' seems to bring the numbers down."

" What does he eat chiefly? " I asked.

" Whatever the red 'un eats, and more besides."

" Well, that must be a pretty varied diet," I said, smiling.

" Billy is partial to anything from toadstools to wild strawberries and cherries. I don't know how he manages it all."

" The worst thing about the way the grey eats is his wastefulness," said Jim. " He'll hop down to yer peastitches, and scatter a dozen pods on the ground for every one he opens. Gardeners starts by blaming tom-tits for what e's done, and ends by saying it's field mice. Why, I even 'eard a farmer down our way say it was eels that came up out of his pond and did the job ! "

I laughed. " I once watched a grey squirrel trying to get at some hen's eggs," I said. " I was sheltering from the rain in a Dutch barn where there was one of those ,corrugated-iron chicken coops-you know, the newly invented rat-proof ones."

Jim nodded. " I've just bought t'missus three on 'em. She were natterin' on about losing 'er chicks."

" I hadn't been there long before I saw a grey squirrel leap down from a tree and run to the coop. He looked exactly like a rat from the distance, except that his coat was grey and, of course, his tail was much bigger." "But not much bushier," Jim interpolated.

" No. You're right there. He hadn't got Billy's fluffy brush, by any means. The squirrel nosed all round the coop, sniffing underneath it. Then he started to scrape a hole. - I could hear the old broody hen inside getting more and more excited, but I trusted to the strength of the coop, and for a few minutes I just watched the raider. Then, thinking that he might touch some catch or spring accidentally and open the coop, I let the dog loose on him, and off he ran."

The keeper picked up the grey squirrel, and silhouetted its head against a light tree trunk : " That's a'most like the head of a rat,", he said. " It's not nearly so finely made as the red's. His body, too, is about twice as big, and coarser in t'bone and fur. That's not a tail neither-it's simply a bit o'rope wi' hairs stuck on it. Ye can tell he's only a tree-rat in disguise."

By this time we had reached the boundary of Jim's territory, and this was where I parted from him.

" Thanks for your company, Jim," I said, " and for all you've told me about the grey squirrel. I'll pass it on to Tim when I see him next."

My meeting with Tim occurred sooner than I had expected. Returning through the wood that same evening, I was surprised to see him standing at the foot of Billy's tree with a stone in his hand. He seemed to be on the point of aiming at Billy himself, whose red fur showed plainly through the dusk, and though I knew this was the last thing he could possibly be doing, I quickened my pace.

" It's our cat, Nixie," he explained, when he saw me. " I'll give her beans for this ! "

Perched thirty feet from the ground , was Billy, gazing fixedly into the eyes of a large black cat. Less than three feet separated the two animals, and the cat was crouching low in preparation for a spring. But it was a different Billy from the one we knew-a distended and defiant Billy. With all his hair on end , and blown out to its fullest extent, he was making a brave effort to look twice as large as life. In addition, he was giving Nixie one of those pieces of his mind which, if they were to be translated , would, perforce, have to be represented by a row of asterisks. But in the depths of his little heart he was mortally afraid.

The noise he was making was sheer bravado , and Nixie , unfortunately for him , knew quite well that it was, and licked her chops in consequence.

It was then that I realised why it was that Billy was standing like Horatius of old , holding the cat at bay, when he might so easily have escaped into the upper branches of the tree.

" The young ones must have arrived," I said to Tim." And Billy knows that his job is to stop Nixie from getting at the nest. But where is his mate? "

" She ran over to that other drey in the sycamore tree," said Tim. " She was carrying summat, an' all. I never saw what it was."

"Probably a youngster. Yes," I said, as I saw the mother-squirrel coming back to the nest which Billy was defending, " she's going to transfer them to the other drey. We must make Nixie come down somehow."

We lobbed stones on to the branch where the cat was sitting, and together set up such a cater-wauling and shouting that Nixie lost her nerve. Unlike Billy, she had nothing to lose by turning tail, and down the tree she came, to find Raq waiting for her.

Away the two of them went, the cat carrying her tail at an angle that was an insult in itself, and Tim and I, having seen the squirrel family safely transferred to their new home, returned to the vardo.

SQUIRRELS AT HOME

ON my return from the smithy, where I had taken Comma to be re- shod, I called at the village shop.

" I'm just baking," Martha informed me, above the noisy tinkling of the door-bell.

In warm, sweet waves the smell of loaves and scones fresh from the oven escaped through the kitchen door, and lapped its way into every nook and cranny of the little shop. Its lure was irresistible, and Martha knew it.

" I'll take half a dozen of those scones, if you can spare them," I said, " although it was the peanuts that I really came in for."

" Certainly, I can spare 'em, an' welcome," returned Martha, not a little flattered by the rapt manner in which Raq and I were sniffing the air.

Reaching behind a large paraffin tin, she pulled out Tim's bag of peanuts, and wrapped them up with the scones.

I climbed on to Comma's broad back again, and we continued our leisurely journey.

Perhaps I have not mentioned before that Comma has a passion for scones as all-consuming as my own. How she acquired this curious taste in the first instance I have never been able to make out, unless it was during the raid which she once made on the larder of some unfortunate Boy Scouts who were camping in her field. This, her first essay in crime , apparently encouraged her , when we were in a busy market-town,to sample the contents of a baker's van, whose doors stood conveniently open right in front of her nose. Four girdle cakes had passed down her spacious gullet, and she was snuffling in a thoughtful way at the eclairs, before either I or the baker had fully realised what was happening. Since that time I have sometimes tempted her with scones when I have particularly wanted her to mend her pace, and I have never known their attraction to fail. She has the discrimination to prefer them buttered, but the good sense never to refuse them at all.

Armed with the peanuts, Tim and I set out for the wood that same evening. Tim walked under the tree in which Billy was sitting, rattling the peanuts in the bag , a sound that Billy knew well. How often had I not enticed him into the vardo by shaking a similar bag as I stood on the steps ! Gradually we lured him down the trunk of the tree. Then we put two or three peanuts at the roots of it, and stepped back a few paces. We had left Raq behind this time, so Billy dropped to the ground very readily.

" We shall get 'im to come down to us yet." said Tim, as the squirrel stuffed the nuts in the pouch of his cheek, and skipped back on to a low branch. " You've missed ,one, Billy," he added, picking up a nut. But Billy wisely went on cracking the shells of the nuts he had pouched, and I almost imagined that he winked at me.

" Have a look inside that shell," I suggested. " I think you'll find that Billy left that one on purpose."

" Yes, it's a bad 'un," said Tim in surprise, as Billy ran up the tree. " How did he know that, Romany ? "

" By the weight of it. If a squirrel passes a nut, you may be sure that it's rotten inside. You sometimes see quite a number of beech or hazel nuts stored away in a hole in a tree, and when you come to crack them there's not a good one amongst them."

Billy had now finished the hors d'oeuvre, and was looking expectantly at us. Putting a nut on my right shoulder I edged under the branch so that I stood directly beneath him, and waited for him to make a move.

" Don't look at him, Tim," I said. " All animals fear the human eye, and Billy is no exception."

Tim averted his head, and immediately I felt the soft pressure of Billy's forepaws on my shoulder. This touch -possibly he remembered the "feel " of my rough jacket -seemed to reassure him, and he let go his last hold on the branch.

" Put your shoulder against mine," I said to Tim, " and put a nut on it."

Billy showed no alarm as Tim sidled up to me, and a second later was sitting contentedly on the boy's shoulder cracking a nut. Tim's face was a treat to see. Billy's tail was tickling the back of his neck so excruciatingly that it was only with a great effort of will that he could resist moving. His delight at having at last got the little creature to conquer his distrust, however, won the day; and for several minutes he stood there, his head held stiffly upright, as though he were balancing a water-jug, watching Billy out of the comer of his eye.

We gave Billy all the nuts he could eat, and two or three more "for the road." With these in his pouch, he whisked back on to the horizontal branch, and made off in the direction of the drey in the sycamore tree.

" Will he give 'em to the young squirrels? " asked Tim.

"Oh no. They're too young for anything but milk just yet. But he will probably share them with his mate," I said.

"What do the babies look like, Romany ? "

" Like young pigs," I said. " They have only a few short stubby whiskers on their little bodies. Their tails are quite bare and straight, and it's a long-time before they curve up like Billy's. Perhaps the Spring showers are needed to warp them a bit."

" Are they blind, too, same as piglets ? "

I nodded. " There goes the mother-squirrel into the drey now." I said.

"Could I climb up to see them little 'uns ? "

" Better not, Tim," I advised him. You saw how Nixie scared them. It would be kinder to let them alone until the young ones are a bit older. Then they'll come out into the open, and we shall see quite a lot of them at various times."

" They won't disappear same as the otters did, then ?"he queried doubtfully.

" No, they won't do that," I assured him, as we turned back towards the vardo. " Squirrels are good parents they mate for life, you know, and when the young ones are beginning to grow up, they don't turn them adrift immediately. They all travel about together as a family for a while, and we may be able to watch the parents teach the youngsters all the tricks they have learned themselves."

TIM PLAYS GULLIVER

DURING the Spring and early Summer, Tim spent several evenings alone in the wood watching Billy and his family. When they had overcome their native fear of anything strange, the young ones came scampering to take peanuts out of his fingers as readily as Billy himself did. The old nest in the sycamore tree, I had noticed, had canted slightly to one side, and some of the sticks had fallen out of place. It looked bedraggled and untidy, and I was not surprised when Tim informed me that the squirrels had deserted it.

" They're in a drey at t'other end of the wood, not far from us." he said, and then he described to me how he had borrowed an old telescope from a school friend. " I can see 'em from me bedroom winder swinging in the top branches. Why didn't they use one of them old dreys, Romany, instead of building a new one ? "

"Oh , squirrels like a change, you know. Besides , I doubt whether they did build the nest they are in now. If it's the one I think it is, it was made by a carrion crow last year, and the squirrels have taken possession now that he has gone."

" Some other animal does that trick," said Tim, wrinkling his forehead in an effort to remember something I had told him. " Instead of digging a burrow, it uses some one else's."

" Perhaps you're thinking of Flash, the Fox," I said.

" But she takes over a large rabbit-hole like the bailiff's man, while the rabbits are still inside. Billy would never think of going near the carrion crow's nest, unless he was sure the bird had left it. The fox uses a rabbit warren as though it were a hotel."

" Mebbe he gobbles up the other hotel guests for his meals," said Tim, with a laugh.

" Not necessarily, " I told him. " The rabbits have their own narrow corridors into which the fox can't follow them. He can't really get much farther in than the entrance-hall. And a wise fox never hunts near his own home-so he may leave the rabbits alone on policy."

" What happens if some other squirrel is living near the place they move to, Romany ? "

"Oh, the one who is there first is annoyed, and unless the newcomer is bigger-like the grey squirrel, for instance-he will try and drive him away. But there are no other squirrels in our wood that I know of, so Billy can move where he likes."

Since Tim was anxious to show me how well he had succeeded in taming the squirrel family, I let him take Raq and me into the corner of the wood near their farm. It was a spot I rarely visited, but I found that my guess about the nature of Billy's new home had been a good one. There they were, ensconced in the carrion crow's nest as comfortably as though they had built it themselves.

When Billy and the youngsters first caught sight of Tim and me , I noticed that they were now shy of me, and that they ran at once to Tim.

As Tim lay on the ground, the little, furry creatures clambered all over him, like the Lilliputians when they first came upon Gulliver lying asleep. They explored his pockets for peanuts with the deftness of long practice, and the funniest moment was when Billy himself fished out an indiarubber from Tim's pocket, and, running to the nearest tree, tried his teeth on it.

" Hi ! stop that," cried Tim excitedly, making a dash for the tree.

He was only just in time. Billy's interest in the rubber did not outlive the, discovery that it was hard and indigestible , so he let it drop from the branch while Tim was still several yards away from the tree.

" How's that ? " Throwing himself out at full length, Tim , brought off a fine left- handed catch, and grinned up at me in triumph.

" Hammond himself would have dropped that one," I laughed. " But if you can make Billy go back to the pavilion you're a better umpire than I am. Did you see the way he licked it before trying his teeth on it?"

" Yes, I did. I hope he liked the taste, an' all," he said.

"I don't think Billy was tasting it, all the same. You see , he does the very same thing to a nut before cracking it. I think it must help him to get a better grip."

" Like spitting on your hands when you're digging ? " suggested Tim.

" Yes, that's the idea. Billy's paws have got very fine hairs on the inside to help him grip slippery surfaces of all kinds. Did you know that he had hairs inside his mouth, too? "

" Has he ? " said Tim.

"Yes, the fur on the cheeks of most animals like Billy, and mice and rats, and rodents of all kinds, seems to go right inside their mouths. What it's for-I can't think."

Leaving the squirrels at their play, we called Raq out of the undergrowth where he was keeping patient watch over a rabbit-run, and continued our walk. It was the only time, although I did not then know it, on which I was to see the squirrel family together. When I passed that way later, the carrion crow's nest was deserted just as the old drey had been, and Tim himself was as much at a loss as I was to know where they had gone to. I consoled him as best I could, but in my heart I feared that we had seen the last of Billy. Squirrels are apt at times to be taken with a strange wander lust , which drives them into travelling miles over strange country, before they find a piece of territory which suits them. Once , a red squirrel, it is true, had caught my eye scuttling along a stone wall near the river-but it was not Billy.

I was therefore all the more delighted when Autumn came to be able to tell Tim that I had seen our old friend once again, and together we went out to look for him.

BILLY'S WINTER NAP

THE wood was silent save for the sound of falling leaves-just a tiny snap and a gentle fluttering to the ground. Now and then a horse-chestnut dropped one of its spiked bombs. It bounced and exploded, showing a beautiful nut, red as mahogany.

Billy was still running about in the tree-tops. He was rather proud of his appearance. The thin coat of summer was fast disappearing, but his bushy tail still had its wonderful curve. I pointed out to Tim that he was growing a little greyer-but that this was customary in winter-time, since it helped to camouflage his movements, for everything around him had begun to put on more sombre tones. When we saw him he was busy burying nuts. He worked quickly , as though time were pressing-as indeed it was-and he rejected our advances a trifle coldly. We had no peanuts with us now; nothing with which to help him stack his larder, and though he had no objection to our company, he did not permit the claims of past friendships to interfere with the business in hand.

"Look, Romany," said Tim. " He's burying nuts in half a dozen different places. Why doesn't he put 'em all in one hole? "

" Perhaps he thinks it prudent not to put all his eggs in one basket," I said. " Hullo ! Here comes another red squirrel."

The newcomer advanced gingerly towards the clearing in which Billy was burying his treasure , and seemed ready to turn and run at the slightest sign of hostility. But, to my surprise, it was Billy who quitted the scene. From a convenient branch, he watched the stranger's movements with bright-eyed interest. Nor did he show any resentment when the stranger unearthed one of the nuts he himself had buried only a moment before.

" Perhaps it's one of his own children, who's grown up now," suggested Tim, " and that's why he isn't angry."

" No." I shook my head. " This squirrel is not a young one, and besides, I doubt whether blood would prove any thicker than water in a case like this. If Billy knew he was being robbed, he would soon be at the interloper's throat. " Tim looked up at me in bewilderment.

" What do you mean, Romany? Can't he see toother squirrel digging them up now."

" Yes. But I don't think he realises that those are his nuts. I don't think he remembers more than a few of the places in which he has hidden them. He buries hundreds, but his finding of them during the winter is more a matter of good luck than good memory."   The stranger seemed disposed to linger in the clearing, but Billy's patience was now wearing thin. Down the tree he came, and made one dash, which sent his enemy skeltering for dear life back the way he had come. Then, Billy settled down once more to his work.

" I should think all those hazel bushes over there have been planted by squirrels," I said. "They have buried the hazel nuts in Autumn, as Billy is doing , now, and then have forgotten to dig them up again. When the outer shell has rotted away, the Spring rains and sunshine have made the kernels sprout like seeds."

" How is it he doesn't starve in Winter if he can't remember where he's buried his food? " asked Tim.

" Oh, he doesn't bury all the nuts he finds," I answered.

" He has one or two main larders besides, in which he stores more than enough to feed him during the cold weather. He manages to remember where these are. Birds and small rodents may rob him of a few nuts while he is asleep, but on the rare occasions when he does come out to do his little bit of shopping, as it were, he usually finds plenty to eat."

" I wish I could see him asleep," said Tim.

It was not long before his wish was realised. One morning some weeks later Jack Frost had limned every branch with whiteness.

Tim and I were returning from a walk when we spied Billy creep into the deep fork of a beech tree where he gathered together a big heap of leaves.

" We're just in time, Tim, to see the last of him." I said, and we climbed a bank to get a better view. His winter hiding-place was very snug and free from draughts, and as he burrowed down into the leaves

and covered himself with them, he curled his long tail round his body and over his nose, and with a sigh, sank into a dreamless sleep.

" Good-bye, Billy,". Tim whispered.

No answering " Vut " came from the beech tree. All we could hear was the wind gently swaying the towering branches rocking Billy to sleep.

DANDY AND STUMPY, THE WRENS

A GOSSAMER HAMMOCK

IT was a perfect April morning as Raq and I walked through the wood to the vardo. Suddenly I noticed that he was limping. Then he lay down and started to bite his front paw.

" Roll over," I said and I soon found a nasty thorn embedded in it.

It was whilst I was doing this that I heard the " Cheep cheep " of a golden-crested wren in a neighbouring fir tree.

When I had finished with Raq, I looked up and saw the bird fly past with a tiny piece of moss in its beak. Boldly it flew to a pine branch about ten feet from the ground. After waiting for a moment, I went along to investigate.

A few days later when Tim brought my milk along, as he always did on Saturdays, I told him that I had a nest to show him.

After searching in the pine trees for some time Tim gave it up, so I pulled down one of the branches and showed him the underside.

He gave his usual low whistle of surprise. " I never thought of looking under the branch, Romany," he said.

" I'm not surprised," I replied, " because it's the only British bird I know which slings its nest like a hammock from a branch. Be careful. It's so frail and dainty that it won't bear touching."

We climbed up on some logs to see it better.

" Won't this frighten her ? " he asked.

" I don't think so. She is one of the bravest birds I have ever met. It takes a lot to upset her."

He had shown great admiration for the cosy nest of the long- tailed tit when we examined it, but the nest of the golden-crested wren made of glistening spider-webs and moss was even more artistic and dainty.

When I myself first found it the birds had just got the foundations made, using long twisted strands of gossamer, and crossing them to form the hammock. Since then, they had been busy fetching moss and weaving it into the silken scaffolding.

We sat down a few yards away from the tree, and in a short time both birds began to feed on the tiny insects they found on the pine branches.

" They are as clever acrobats as tom-tits," Tim said as we watched them hanging in every con-ceivable position.

They chattered at us as though they would know our business but showed no fear. One came within a couple of yards of us , so we had a splendid chance of seeing its beautiful plumage. It was olive-green, buff and brown, and had a crest of lemon-yellow, merging into orange-flame. This was more conspicuous because of a band of black feathers on either side of the crest.

" That's the cock, Tim, his mate is not quite so smart because she has no black feathers." Tim at once christened him " Dandy."

He was surprised when Dandy alighted on a thin branch and did not weigh it down. I explained how very light these birds were, and being a farmer's boy, I thought he would understand better if I said that the bird only weighed about seventy grains of wheat.

The marvellous thing was that Dandy and his tiny mate had actually flown here from Norway-braving the dangers of the North Sea.

Tim was thrilled when I described their difficult journey and how they always flew by night.

"What happens if there's a big wind on, " he asked.

" We shall never know how many little creatures lose their lives in bad weather," I replied.

" That will be over three hundred miles they've flown to get here," Tim remarked. " We've just been learning it at school."

The following day we visited the nest again and saw both birds carrying feathers. On one of his journeys, Dandy was almost blinded by the fluffy feathers he carried in his bill, and had to perch on a branch to get a better grip of them before he could reach the nest. As he flew between the trunks of two pine trees, a slight breeze caught him unawares, struck the feathers like a sail, and almost upset his balance. Manfully he stuck to his feathers and finally reached the nest.

We were interrupted by a loud burst of song, so big that it was difficult to believe that it came from one of the ordinary wrens not far away.

" What lung power it has for its size," I remarked.

" If one of your cows could bellow proportionately, we should have to put cotton-wool in our ears."

" Especially after it has had its calf taken away," Tim remarked.

I suggested that we should look for the wren's nest, so that Tim could compare it with its cousin's-the one we had just been watching.

Wrens build in all kinds of places-ivy growing round trees, or the overhang of an ivy-clad bank, in the niches of a rock, or a hole in a post. I once found a nest in a coil of rope in a shed, and another in the pocket of a man's coat that hung in an outhouse. Tim got busy and at last found the nest in the roots of ivy around a tree. The wrens were very indignant at our presence and made more noise than ever.

" There are no eggs," Tim said disappointedly.

I put my fingers in gently. " No feathers either, Tim. That shows that this won't be the proper nest. I have often told you how wrens build two or three nests, but only use the feather-lined one for the eggs. Some say that Mr. Wren builds the others to sleep in himself whilst she sits on the eggs, but whatever they are used for, I have often watched them and I know that the work of building the nests is shared by both birds."

" It's queer that they don't finish the others off," he remarked.

" Yes. It's queer, too, that a thrush lines her nest with mud, but that her cousin, the blackbird, puts fibres on top of the mud. Both birds nest at the same time, and in similar places.

I was interested to hear what name Tim would give the cock bird, and when he chose " Stumpy " for this plump little bird I thought it suited him well.

During our search, we came across another " cock's nest," as Tim called it, and the more angry Stumpy became, the nearer I knew we must be to the real nest. He little knew that by expressing his displeasure he was giving us a clue to its position. About six feet from the ground, built in a split in the trunk of a tree, we at last found the feather-lined nest in which the eggs would be laid.

" Now we've two nests to watch," Tim said.

I myself had intended to come again and see how the two wrens were getting on, but I was glad to feel that Tim was just as keen to come too.

TIM'S CAP COMES IN USEFUL

WE often visited the pine-wood to see how the egg laying was going on. So tiny were the eggs of the golden-crested wren that we dare not touch them in case we broke them. They had light brown markings on a yellow background. The eggs that Stumpy's mate laid were larger and were white with pink markings. Once when she was on the nest Tim put his finger inside and she promptly pecked him but did not fly off.

We touched the nest as little as possible , because wrens, though they seem bold enough, will often forsake their nests if anyone interferes with them in any way.

One day we sat near the nest listening for the tiny squeaking of any young birds that might have been hatched. Stumpy came and peered at us, and as he scolded, he held his absurd little tail at an impertinent angle. I was surprised that Tim had never heard the story of how the wren got its tail.

" Once upon a time," I began, " all the birds held a parliament to decide which bird among them should be king. It was agreed that the bird which flew the highest should be acknowledged the ruler. Each flew in turn, and finally the golden eagle mounted up and up far outdistancing all the others. But just as he reached his apex, and was celebrating his triumph, to everyone's surprise, a wren popped out from his shoulder feathers.

It mounted still higher and so won the coveted title. The eagle got into such a rage that it dashed the little wren to the ground and broke its tail."

I explained to Tim that a wren does not need a long tail because it stays put most of its time in hedges and on walls, and never makes long journeys. It never uses its tail as some birds do as a balancing pole, back-pedalling brake or rudder.

While his mate was sitting on her eggs we heard Stumpy singing lustily some distance away. When we went to find him we discovered him near one of the unfinished nests. As we got near he showed the same concern and excitement as he did when we visited his real nursery. Once he went inside the nest and stayed there a few minutes, but being a gallant bird he was soon off again to keep his mate well supplied with food.

When the youngsters were first hatched, we could not see much of them except their large heads and scraggy necks as they poked them up to receive the minute insects their parents brought them. As their eyes were not open, they did not took very attractive. Both Stumpy and his mate resented our presence and never made us feel at all welcome. Dandy, on the other hand, was much more friendly and came and searched for food quite close to us.

As the young gold crests grew bigger we worried as to whether their gossamer strands would stand their weight any longer. We often saw their wagging heads as they lifted them for food, and when Tim tried to count them, he said they were all "in such a ruck" that he couldn't tell "toothier from which." Finally he counted ten.

As luck would have it, we happened to be there one day when a calamity occurred . Dandy returned with food for his mate, who was sitting on the edge of the nest. When he alighted there was a sudden sagging, the little hammock snapped at one end, and the whole nursery began to collapse.

"Quick, Tim your cap," I called as the parents fluttered out of the debris.

Before the words were out of my mouth Tim had jumped forward and caught the youngsters in his cap. " Well caught," I said.

" Cheep, Cheep, Cheep ,Cheep," came the piteous cries of the parent birds.

I promised to see Tim's mother about my getting him a new cap and then tied the two sides of it with string, so that it resembled a hammock. I then put the remains of the old nest and the youngsters in the cap, and Tim helped me to sling it up in the same position. But we had overlooked one thing and that was its weight. It pulled down the thin pine branch. We got over this difficulty, however, by using a stout pole. Then with anxious feelings, we hid ourselves behind a tree and waited to see what the parents would do. Dandy's mate was not in the least upset about it, and to our great delight returned and fed her babies as soon as the nest was fixed up. Dandy himself was more timid, but when at last he did return, we felt that we need not worry about the little family any more.

We paid several more visits before we finally saw the whole family launched into the world. It was a sight not easily forgotten to see nine little animated fluff balls- almost replicas of their parents- sitting on a branch in half sunlight and half shadow, nodding their flame-coloured heads. When Dandy called from a neighbouring tree the little cascade of flame and olive-green balls vanished into the wood.

Tim gave a sigh of regret. We had grown fond of these little teaspoonfuls of life, and he knew that this meant that we should not see them again. " I'll leave my cap, Romany," he remarked.

" As a souvenir of happy watchings," I said. " Let's go and see what Stumpy is up to," I added.

Stumpy had not such a big family to look after, but both birds were in a fluster when we arrived because all seven of them were scattered about and difficult to feed.

It was clever the way the parents lured those farthest away to come to a certain branch to be fed. No shepherd-dog ever worked harder to collect his flock, and by teatime they had managed to get the whole family together.

Later we saw Stumpy busy searching for insects near the stream. I told Tim that some people have seen wrens actually wade into the water and disappear from sight as they search for water insects.

" You know his relation who does that, Tim ? "

He nodded. "The dipper."

Both little wren families then became scattered. Stumpy's family broke up at once and each went his own way. For some time we used to see a few of the golden crests flying about with tom-tits and cole-tits. We often passed the pine tree on our rambles and saw Tim's cap still swaying in the breeze, and as the leaves fell we saw it more and more clearly. Each time we passed, it reminded us of the day when we had saved the lives of the little family.

A JOURNEY IN THE VARDO

FOR the first few miles I made Comma trot at a good pace, partly because I wanted her to work off any friskiness due to having had little work lately, and partly because the country was so familiar to Tim that he did not think it very interesting. When we reached country that was new to him I let her go her own pace. I knew that it would take us a good week to reach the islands even if we went "all out" but I was not anxious to get there too soon, nor to overwork Comma.

When Tim seemed a bit impatient I reminded him that though most of the sea-birds would be sitting, we should find them more interesting to watch when the eggs were hatched.

He understood at once what I meant, knowing farm life as he did.

" When birds get scared and leave their eggs they take a long time to come back, don't they, Romany ? But they won't leave their youngsters for long however scared they are."

So we both decided that we would take things easily and see all we could on the way. Whether we did ten or twenty miles a day was not nearly as important as seeing the country and its wild life.

Considering how much he was looking forward to the sea, Tim settled down very contentedly to jogging along the lanes.

Having lived on a farm too he was very quick to point out good straight furrows, well-kept hedges, or hedges that had been badly layered. He knew when a cottage was well thatched and often remarked on the cows and the growing lambs. As we jogged along I pointed to a plover wheeling over a field about fifty yards ahead of us.

" How long does it generally take us to find a plover's nest, Tim ?"

" A couple of hours, mebbe, if we haven't got a line on it."

While waiting for a plover to return to her well camouflaged nest on the ground our usual method had always been to hide behind a bush. When she returned we drew an imaginary line from the nest to a tree beyond it. This is what Tim meant by " getting a line " on it. With such a clue it was fairly easy then to walk up and find the nest.

"I think we shall find this nest in a few minutes, Tim. Keep your eyes open."

When we reached the field we looked over the hedge and saw the hen bird sitting on her eggs. She took not the slightest notice of us. Even the cock bird who was acting as a " spotter " up aloft was not a bit perturbed, and sent down no alarm signals to her.

"Prasta, Comma, lass." I called.

The sitting plover then became more alert. I told Tim to jump down and walk along by the hedge. The moment his foot touched the ground the cock plover gave the "danger "call and his mate flew off the nest.

Tim seemed a bit mystified about it all.

" I wanted to show you how these wild birds take little notice of cars, carts, or lorries, but are afraid of human beings. These plovers made no move even when the vardo was in full view, but they were scared stiff of you. A cart says to them, 'You need not fear the person driving it; he has other work to do than think about you."

" For years they have seen carts moving about the fields, and no danger has ever come from them. But when they see a man, they know that be may shoot them or take their eggs, and so they take no chances when he is about."

Tim laughed when I told him of a well-known photographer of birds who had rigged up a dummy cow in which he could move about with his camera. He used to move along slowly as though he were a cow grazing, and the birds were not in the least afraid."

Tim chuckled. " I've noticed that birds take no notice of our cattle in the fields. A starling will even perch on the back of a sheep." He was silent for a moment. " The next time one of our cows dies I'll ask my father if we can make a dummy cow of him, Romany. But I wouldn't like to be inside if an enemy attacked it."

" I know what I would do, Tim."

" Hop it, I reckon," he laughed.

The day was so hot that we pulled up under a shady tree to have our lunch. Clambering up through the long grass the white bryony was twining itself around the hedge-now a mass of creamy hawthorn blossom. Tim was more interested in the tiny scarlet insects that crawled over the cow-parsley in the ditch than in some of the wild flowers I was showing him.

Comma was so bothered by the flies that I told Tim to look round for an elderberry tree.

" If you can find a bit of early blossom all the better."

He called Raq and went along the hedge side and it was not long before his " Coo-ee " told me that he had found some elderberry. Soon we had a small bunch of leaves tied on Comma's bridle.

I explained how flies hate the smell of elderberry and that many people hang it up instead of fly-paper in the summer. Though it is not an attractive tree, it seems to be able to grow anywhere. Even the birds don't like nesting or roosting in it.

" Mother makes me pick the fruit for her elderberry wine," he said.

" Yes, and once upon a time ladies used the water in which the flowers were boiled for their complexions."

Towards evening we pulled up at a farm and were readily given permission to camp in a lane nearby. We backed the vardo into it, choosing a place where even if it rained all night the ground would not get soft. There were cobble-stones to give Comma's hoofs a grip, and to prevent the wheels from skidding. Tim helped to unharness Comma, and after grooming her well with brush and curry-comb, we sat and waited whilst she munched her oats and bran-a sound which always delights me.

We then turned her loose into a field. The first thing she did was to roll on her back and kick up her legs vigorously but awkwardly.

" My father likes to see our horses do that, Romany. He says that if they roll like that after a hard day's work they are ready for another spot of work."

Our next job was to get a fire going, and while Tim found the kindling, I fetched water from the pump and brought out the bread and cheese.

There was a time when Tim would have put the kettle on the flames, but he has now learnt that the best heat comes from the hot ash. He learnt by bitter experience that a frying-pan placed on the flames meant spoilt bacon.

Meanwhile Raq was enjoying a roll on the grass, pushing himself along with sheer pleasure. He loves rolling in snow too.

" I wonder why horses and dogs roll over and cows and sheep never do," Tim said as we ate our supper.

" It would be a very serious thing if a sheep rolled over on its back, especially if it was expecting a lamb. It couldn't turn over on its legs again."

" That's true, and I've never seen our pigs rolling about, either."

" They like to wallow in thick mud, don't they ? " Tim made no move to go to bed until we had discussed rabbits, foxes, otters, badgers, goats, and weasels and come to the conclusion that none of them ever rolled on their backs.

" But our cat does, Romany."

" You're right, Tim, but she doesn't roll, she wriggles elegantly."

" Aye, it's a wriggle right enough."

Before going to bed I put a big stone on the ash of the fire to keep it from blowing about.

" Now we'll roll in, shall we, Tim? " I said.

SPOOK-THE BARN OWL

THE GHOSTLY VISITOR

TIM was in the byre helping to feed the cows when I found him.

It was November, and for many days my vardo had been wrapped in mist. No birds trilled in the hedge, and only the robin could be heard breaking the silence of Nature's sleep.

When at last the sun came out, I thought a ramble would be enjoyable. Raq must have thought so too, for as I came down the vardo steps he capered about, wagging his tail furiously. Perhaps he sensed that I was going farther afield than we had been doing, or perhaps he had seen me packing up a few sandwiches. Together we walked towards the farm. As it was a bright morning, the cows were turned out of the byre for a short time so that they could stretch their legs and get a drink at the big stone trough. After the warmth of the byre they were not eager to stay out very long, and I noticed that each of the twenty-six of them found its way back to its own stall of its own accord.

When I told Tim my plans, he rushed into the farm kitchen to get his mother to pack him up some food too, and within half an hour we were bidding Mrs. Fletcher good-bye.

"You mustn't expect to see much in this weather, Tim, I said, not wanting to raise his hopes too much.

"Raq may get a sniff at a grouse or two."

As we passed through the stackyard a flock of small birds rose from a heap of old chaff. I waited to see if Tim could identify them.

" Sparrows, hen chaffinches, and those green-and-brown ones are linnets, but I'm surprised that they go about with common sparrows," he answered.

" Yes, but don't forget that they are all related-all belong to the finch family. They always go about in flocks during the winter. Quite a family gathering, isn't it ?"

As Raq squeezed under the gate into one of the stubble fields a number of small birds rose from the ground and whirled themselves up into an ash tree. " Now then, Tim? "

"Cock chaffinches," he replied. " Not a hen among em."

"Yes. A bachelor party."

"I never can understand why it is that chaffinches split up like that each autumn-the cocks going their own way and the hens living with the sparrows."

" It is a bit queer," I replied.

As we climbed steadily towards the moor, we kept halting and looking down on the fields and ploughed land, deserted save for an odd horse or two, some sheep, and a few starlings who were probing the ground to find insect life which had been disturbed by the grazing sheep. We missed the ceaseless chatter of spring and summer birds and the hum of insect life.

Calling Raq, we climbed over a dry-stone wall built with great skill without any mortar or cement. I could not expect Tim to be interested in this lost art, as the Fletchers' farm was surrounded by these walls. " My father and my grandfather can make them , but we use wire fences on the farm nowadays," he remarked.

Sighing inwardly, I knew that he was right-the art of dry-walling is being forgotten. I like to see the old stones weathered by the years, and the mosses growing on them. Those lovely things never grow on a wire fence.

" And think, Tim, what refuges these walls are for all kinds of birds and beasts-robins, wheatears, wagtails, titmice, wrens, rats, stoats and weasels-all hide in dry-walls. Look, Raq is sniffing at a hole. I shouldn't be surprised if there's a rabbit inside."

" Here, Raq," Tim called. " You can't scratch him out of there. Avaki."

Beyond the wall the bracken and the heather had mastered the grass, and the bracken was waging a winning fight against the heather, or, more correctly, the ling. Raq put up a couple of mallard ducks and a drake, and as they rose from a boggy pool fringed with short reeds, it was amusing to see his aggrieved look when, instead of taxiing along the surface of the pool, they flew straight upwards, giving him no chance of a chase.

" I rather think both those ducks have their eye on Mr. Drake. He doesn't deserve so much attention."

When Tim asked what I meant, I explained that drakes don't make good fathers. The cock partridge looks after the young ones with almost as much care as its mate does, but the mallard drake refuses to help in the nursery at all.

For the next hour or two we walked on, but saw nothing very thrilling, Once we spotted a raven in the distance, but he was too far off for us to see much of him.

" I'll bet he knows every rock and cave on these moors," said Tim.

" He does-as well as you know your farm. Shall we try and photograph him later on ? He usually nests in March."

Tim's eyes sparkled, but I cut short what he would have said by calling Raq sharply to heel and crouching down suddenly in the grass. Tim followed suit as two birds flew at great speed just above the top of the heather.

" Merlins on the hunt," I whispered.

" I hope they won't see that lark" Tim said, pointing to a bird flying over an open patch of moor. Suddenly the lark realised his deadly peril, for he had no refuge into which to dive, and he made a desperate attempt to reach some thick tufts of heather on the right of us.

"He'll never get there, Romany," Tim cried, for the two hawks were gaining on him rapidly.

I was about to get up and shout, and let Raq loose to distract them, when suddenly the lark changed its course and made straight towards us. Tim in his excitement had jumped up, which made the hawks slow up a little. The next second the lark literally threw itself into the heather hardly a yard from where I was crouching. The hawks banked steeply and vanished as quickly as they had come.

" Phew ! That was a near one, and no mistake !"

We both crouched low so as not to frighten the lark out of its hiding place, where we imagined it would be cowering in terror after the great fright it had experienced. When we crawled along to have a look at it Tim laughed outright.

" Why, the little beggar is preening its feathers, Romany."

It was true. Instead of crouching in terror before us, it was actually rearranging a few feathers that were out of place, though it had just escaped a violent death by a fraction of a second.

As we crawled back again Tim said, " Well, that beats everything."

Dusk was beginning to fall, so I whistled to Raq and we turned homeward.

" I believe we saved its life, all the same, Tim. I'm sure it saw us, and knew that its only hope was to hide near us. I remember a rabbit once running almost into my arms when being chased by a stoat, and once I saw a chaffinch fly right into Jim's kitchen when a sparrow hawk was after him. The hawk dashed after it, but it mistook the window for an opening, and broke its neck against the thick window-pane."

" Serve him right ! " said Tim emphatically. " Anyway it's been worth while coming up here, if only to save that bird's life "-a sentiment I heartily endorsed.

It was getting dark as we neared the farm. Floating up to us came Mrs. Fletcher's voice as she locked up her ducks in their pen.

" That'll keep Flash out," said Tim as we heard a door slam and the quackings ceased.

" The worst thing about a fox is that he is not content with one nice plump hen or duck. He seems to go quite mad when he gets among them, and snaps the heads off a score of them," I said.

Tim told me that his father feared that a fox was visiting the farm each night, because their dogs had been very restless lately.

" We'll have to look round for his tracks, Tim. They shouldn't be hard to find. Then we'll have some proof," I said.

We had just got into the stackyard and turned round the comer of the Dutchbarn , when an un-earthly screech made us both duck down involuntarily. Above our heads on ghostly wing a light-coloured owl flew into the darkness beyond. Even Raq was scared, and crept closer to me.

" Gosh ! That gave me a turn, Romany," Tim said with a laugh.

" Yes, I wasn't prepared for it either. But just think Tim-it's a barn owl, and we may get a chance of watching it if it stays here."

" A barn owl ? " echoed Tim.

" Yes. If it does stay it will be a grand help to your father. He'll have fewer rats and mice about the place in a month or two."

"It'll scare my mother if it screeches like that when she's locking up the poultry at night," he said, laughing. " She'll think it's a spook, Romany."

And that is how the barn owl got its name of Spook. To our great delight Spook took up residence in an old barn which was only used when there was a bumper crop of hay, and it was welcomed as an honoured guest. When Mr. Fletcher saw how interested Tim and I were in it, he gave special orders to his men that Spook was not to be disturbed.

Mrs. Fletcher seemed a bit doubtful about the fate of her young chickens, but I soon persuaded her that Spook would do a lot of good work in the farmyard.

WE INVESTIGATE THE BARN

I WAS as excited as Tim at the prospect of Spook being such a near neighbour. Brown and tawny owls are plentiful, and can be seen in almost every wood. The long-eared owl, though more shy, haunts the woodlands, but a barn owl is much more rare, though a few years ago it was more common.

During the first few weeks after we had seen Spook, Tim came down frequently to the vardo to fetch me up to the farm. We found a snug place in the Dutch barn which was close to Spook's barn, and there on the hay we used to lie, with Raq curled up comfortably beside us. As long as he could rest his soft muzzle on some part of my body he was content. One evening we lay there keeping our eyes glued on the slit in the old wall of Spook's barn. It seemed a long time before we saw her flying towards us on noiseless wings. She stood in the entrance for a few minutes, and we had a perfect view of her.

" She's not nearly as big as the brown owl, is she, Romany ? " Tim observed.

" No. She's only about a foot or so long. Look at her beautiful plumage."

The evening light fell on her breast and undersides, which were gleaming white, while her wings and back were a delicate orange-buff shade.

" Use these, Tim," I said, handing him my binoculars.

" Her big eyes look almost black," he observed; " and she's got feathers right down her legs, but she's not a nice shape, Romany."

I knew what he meant. There are some birds whose shape is a delight to the eye, quite apart from the colour of their plumage. A swallow has a pleasing streamlined appearance; so has a hawk; and a blackbird with its yellow bill and well-groomed black feathers is very shapely and smart.

"No, Tim," I agreed. " She's a bit top-heavy and knock-kneed, but she's a beautiful bird all the same."

He laughed. " Aye. That's it-I couldn't think what made her look a bit unsteady on her pins."

But when Spook rose into the air again we forgot all about her lack of graceful symmetry, and only saw that she was a lovely lightsome thing, as unsubstantial as thistledown; and when she turned and dived it seemed as though she had not a bone in her body.

Later on we were so busy talking that the next thing we knew was a shrill piercing scream splitting the gathering darkness. A shiver ran down our spines. Even Raq opened his eyes inquiringly, and we could hear roosting hens in the nearby poultry-house muttering uneasily on their perches , as though they thought the bogey-man had come.

" It's worse than the vixen we heard in the wood that night," Tim said.

I remembered that night well, when we heard the silence of the pinewood shattered by the ghoulish lovesong of a vixen answering the call of a distant dog-fox.

" Yes. When next we hear a badger giving her solo in the mating season, or the quavering Hoo-hoo-hooter-hoo of the brown owl, we shall think it soothing after Spook's screech."

As the days passed and we kept seeing Spook launching herself into the air from her window sill, we knew that she was satisfied with her new abode, and had determined to take up her permanent residence there.

"I wouldn't like to live in that dusty, cobwebby old barn," Tim said," with the calves shuffling about underneath."

I laughed. " But you forget that Spook looks at it very differently from you. You like a well furnished house with plenty of bedrooms and living rooms, but all Spook wants to know is whether she has found a sleeping place with plenty of rats and mice running round about."

" She's got that right enough." he laughed.

As we lay quietly in the hay we could hear the mice rustling in the corn stacks, and could often see them darting out from beneath the cake bins at the end of the byre. They are very fond of the crumbs of linseed cake on which the dairy cows are fed in winter when they cannot get out to the grass.

One evening, having made sure that Spook was out hunting, Tim and I made our way up into her barn. Climbing the ladder, we flashed a torch around amongst the dust and cobwebs until we came across a pile of pellets on the floor in one corner. We then knew that somewhere on a rafter or ledge above them, Spook had her sleeping perch.

" She's found some good meals, anyway," said Tim, picking up one of the pellets.

"Yes. You and I chew our food and are rather particular about what we swallow. We put gristle or bone on the side of our plates. But Spook catches a rat and swallows the lot-fir , bones , ears, everything."

" It's a wonder she doesn't get indigestion," said he , laughing.

She would if Nature did not sort out her food, after she had swallowed it. She has marvellous inside machinery that wraps up everything that is of no use to her. She hiccoughs, and up comes the little parcel of rubbish and falls on the floor. Hawks can do the same thing.

"Don't you wish you could do that, Raq ? " Tim said, patting the dog affectionately.

" Yes. If Raq eats anything that doesn't agree with him Nature doesn't wrap it up in a nice neat pellet of fine tissue paper. He just gives a heave and up it comes." Tim was thoughtful for a moment. Then he said:

" Either way is better than castor oil," and he made awry face.

Having been on so many adventures with me, Tim of course understood that it was not until the Spring that we should have the real excitement of watching Spook's mating operations- I thought it wise, however, to start making a few preparations. First of all we fetched some hay to lie on, and left it near the top of the ladder.

" Later on," I said, " we'll bring up a plank of wood to screen ourselves, but first of all we shall have to leave it lying about for her to get used to it."

As Spook would make her nest on the floor, we should need to have some sort of screen ready to hide behind.

Later that evening, while we were having supper together in the vardo and discussing our plans, we kept hearing the hoot of a brown owl as it flew overhead.

"We might try to find her nest, too, when April comes," I said. " Then you'll be able to compare the two nests."

Tim was very thrilled at the prospect, and said that when the time came he would explore every likely-looking old tree stump he passed. I reminded him that brown owls sometimes choose a hole in the face of a quarry.

"We might with a bit of luck even come across a long-eared owl's nest," I went on. " He prefers a second-hand home."

When Tim looked mystified, I explained that a long-eared owl likes to use a nest that has been deserted by a sparrow hawk, carrion crow , jay , or even a rook.

" I'll keep my eyes open for that, too," he. remarked.

" If you see a squirrel's drey up in the fork of a tree, don't pass that, either. Last year a pair of magpies built a nest in Nab's Wood-you know the sort-a regular fortress of thorns with a domed top and entrance at the side. I took no notice of it until one evening, to my surprise, I saw a long-eared owl sitting near it. I think the owls had turned the magpies out. I did not hear much of them except at night-a quavering note-a different hoot from the brown owls'."

When we had finished supper I turned down the lamp to a faint glimmer and piled wood on the fire. There is nothing Tim likes better than to sit with me quietly in the firelight, with Raq snuggling up against us as we plan our adventures.

I told him that we would have to choose a night when the moon was full to enable us to see Spook's doings better.

" Well, even if we don't manage to find the other nests, we've got Spook," he kept saying.

" That's true, " I said. " Now she is settled in the barn we are sure of her. Though we can tell within a field or two where to find other birds, we've always to spend so much time searching for their nests before we can start our observations."

Tim nodded. "Aye, it took us hours to find that wheatear's nest amongst those stones on the moor, even when we were quite close to it. He did lead us a nice dance, didn't he? "

" Yes. Spook has saved us all that trouble. Then too we need not wait till the eggs are laid before we can get near, as we always have to do with other birds." . I walked through the wood with Tim until I saw the lights of the farm kitchen faintly showing through a crack in the curtain. " When I get to bed I'm going to make a list of the nights when there's a moon," was Tim's last remark. " I'll put them down as Spook's nights."

He gave Raq a final pat, and vanished into the darkness. When I heard the click of the gate followed by the hoot of a brown owl, I immediately cupped my hands and replied to it. That was our way of saying Good-night to each other.

AN OWL'S MENU

IT was several weeks before I was able to go and watch Spook again. In fact, Christmas was over and it was well into the New Year. Meanwhile, Tim came down frequently to see me, and kept me fully informed about her doings. One evening he came down looking very depressed, and said that he had not seen her for over a week.

" But you forget the weather we are having, Tim. Spook lives on mice."

" Do you mean because everything, is frozen up ? We can't get on the land to plough, and it has taken my father all his time to find jobs for the men to do."

We were standing on the vardo step, and the January wind blew keenly from the north-east. Frost still sparkled on the roof, and there was ice in the lane ruts.

" Shall we go up to the moors and look for grouse eggs? " I said casually.

Tim's eyes opened wide with astonishment and bewilderment.

" Grouse eggs in January ?" he said incredulously.

I laughed and said, " It's no use going to look for something we know isn't there."

He still looked puzzled, and then he burst out laughing.

" I see what you mean, Romany. Mice don't come out in frost. That's why I haven't seen Spook. But how does she keep alive ?"

I replied that I thought she spent most of her time fasting and sleeping, waiting for the thaw.

The next day the frost vanished, and when Tim arrived I knew by his face that the news about Spook was good.

" She was out again last night," he said with glee.

As we talked round the fire I suggested that the time had now arrived when we should get Spook accustomed to the look of us.

" We don't know yet whether she's a bold bird or nervous, and we can't afford to take any risks. We'll go up each day and sit and chat under her window, and then we'll try getting nearer to her. We'll sit on the barn ladder, and then gradually show ourselves."

We chose a nice morning and settled ourselves under her window for a chat, making a point of talking louder as our conversation proceeded.

" I wonder why barn owls live near people. Do you think they like company ? " Tim asked.

I answered him by asking another question: " Sparrows, house-martins, mice, rats, swallows and robins always live near people. Do you think they like company, Tim? "

He thought for a moment, and then said, " They like our food better, I reckon."

Tim had answered his own question. Spook lived where mice and rats were most plentiful. Houses and farm buildings provide good nesting sites for many birds who know that there are always scraps of food or stored food handy for them.

" They settle where they can live most easily, Tim."

We went on talking, hoping that Spook would get used to our chatter and realise that it meant no danger to her. We even tried a chorus or two-which was enough to scare anyone, because Tim is no musician and always sings on one note, no matter what tune I may be singing. As I feared, our choruses had more effect on Mrs. Fletcher than on Spook, for she came out from the kitchen, her hands covered in flour, to see what was the matter.

She had always been ready to let Tim join me on my expeditions, but this was the first time she had an opportunity of seeing us at close quarters, and she naturally looked mystified.

" Oh, it's you, is it! " she said with a smile." I heard t'squealin', an' I thought Fletcher must be ringing a pig."

We laughed heartily, and explained what we were doing. As she went into the house she said, " Well, if Spook or whatever you call her will stand that, she'll stand owt."

" Your mother hasn't a high opinion of our musical ability, Tim, and I don't think she is quite happy at having Spook so near her poultry. She still thinks all owls are a danger to a farm."

" Aye," Tim replied. " She is a bit uneasy like, but I keep tellin' her that Spook is the best visitor we've had for years."

Mrs. Fletcher's attitude worried me, for though I knew that she would never dream of interfering with the bird, I felt that I would like her to be enthusiastic about Spook's visit. I therefore thought out a plan which might reassure her, and unfolded it to Tim when she had left us. " We'll have to show your mother some definite proof, Tim, and in order to do so we've got to learn a bit more about what Spook really does eat. At the moment we can open the pellets and say, 'That looks like a rat bone or that belongs to a mouse,' but that is as far as we can go. The only real way to find out is to catch a rat and a mouse ourselves."

" Cut 'em up and sort out the bones, you mean? " he asked eagerly.

" No. You've plenty of rat traps about the farm, and there are lots of dead frogs about, too. We'll put them in lime, and only the bones will then remain."

" I'll get a bit of board and fix them on it, so that we can see them better."

" That's a good idea. But your mother is not the only person we'll have to convince, Tim. I've seen owls on many a gamekeeper's gibbet."

" Not on Jim's gibbet, surely ?" he asked apprehensively.

" No. Jim has more sense than that."

The wind became so keen that we were obliged to get up from our seat beneath Spook's window and make our way back to the vardo for a hot drink. While Tim took the bucket to the stream for some water, I reached for a book from my shelf and turned over the pages.

Later I said, " Tim, listen to what this naturalist says about owls. ' In eleven hundred and four owl pellets which I analysed I found 997 field voles, 726 mice, 409 shrews, 205 rats, 97 sparrows, 81 other birds, 10 water voles, 9 frogs, 5 moles, 3 beetles, 2 rabbits and a squirrel.' "

As I read on, Tim's eyes opened wider and wider with astonishment. " Wait a minute, Romany." He fished in his pocket for a pencil and paper, and I read it to him slowly so that he could put it down.

All the time we were eating our meal he kept referring to his paper and making various calculations. Then in a puzzled voice he said, " How could there be more than eleven hundred mice and things if there were only eleven hundred pellets ?"

" Don't you sometimes have more than one cake for your tea, Tim ?" I asked.

He laughed. " Oh! I see. In one pellet there might be six voles, a sparrow, and a frog."

From then onwards we decided to pick up any dead birds or animals we saw lying about, as we did not want, to kill them unless we could help it.

" Keep an eye on all your cats, Tim. Waylay them whenever you find they've got hold of a mouse. We mustn't kill any useful or harmless things. We'll start on voles, mice and rats first of all."

Meanwhile we continued visiting Spook. The calves got used to our presence, though we made quite a hubbub at times. Finally we climbed up the ladder leading to the loft, and stood so that Spook could just see our heads and shoulders. To our delight she was not a bit scared.

It was a great day when we dared to venture farther into her loft. She was dozing on her rafter with her back turned to us.

" There she is, Romany," Tim whispered. We held our breath as Spook turned and looked at us without fear.

Her head had completed a perfect half-circle, and yet her body had never moved.

Tim looked disappointed when I motioned to him to follow me down the ladder again, but I dared not risk staying longer.

" Gosh ! " said Tim, " did you see the way she screwed her head round? She looked like a chap who's got his trousers on back to front."

I laughed. Spook certainly did look comical.

" How useful she must find it, to be able to look round without turning her body ! Mice have such quick sight. And what a wide range of vision it gives her, too. I meant to tell you to look at her claws."

" I did, Romany. She had three in front and one behind, just like a thrush."

It was time for Tim to be getting some work done, so I told him to remind me to tell him more about her claws some other time.

SPOOK ON THE HUNT

THOUGH the farm buildings seemed alive with rats and mice, it was some time before we could secure our specimens.

" When I don't want a mouse, I see hundreds about. I tried all Sunday morning," Tim remarked when he came down to the vardo to see me. As he helped me to dry my dishes I asked him if he had noticed that all wild creatures were more tame on Sundays. He looked up at me to see if I was serious, and I went on to explain that one reason was that everything is more quiet on a farm on Sundays, when no tractors are used and no men are at work.

" I've an idea, too, Tim, that wild creatures sense somehow when a hunting animal is anywhere near them and make themselves scarce."

"Our cows soon know when a stranger goes into the byre, even if they don't see him. They get fidgety. Perhaps they smell him."

I went on to tell him that I had seen some rabbits sitting quietly out in a field whilst a stoat - their great enemy - ran leisurely down the side of the hedge. Probably they would have dashed into their burrows if he had run towards them, but my theory was that the rabbits somehow knew that he was not out on a hunting expedition that day.

I went on to ask him how it was that savage dogs knew when people were afraid of them, just as they seem to sense anyone who is fond of them.

"Aye. Tom Haxby keeps his airedale on a chain because he shows his teeth and attacks anyone who goes near him. I'm not afraid of him, and he lets me go near and stroke him."

" That's it, Tim. Some people say that when we are afraid or angry our bodies give off a different scent, and that animals, having keen noses, can tell this."

" You mean that the rabbits knew the stoat wasn't after them because the scent from his body told them ? "

" Yes. They recognised it as a non-hunting scent. Perhaps the reason you couldn't catch a mouse was that they scented you as a hunter."

Our conversation was interrupted by the rumbling of a fallen bucket under the vardo. Raq had been sound asleep, lying against one of the wheels. He bounced up the steps with his eyes full of expectancy, and after rubbing affectionately against my legs, he gave Tim a good lick, which was his way of asking us to take him out.

We went up to the farm by a roundabout way so that he might get a longer run. This tired him so much that he didn't mind when I shut him in the stable on our arrival at the farm.

It seemed strange, as Tim had said, that though the place seemed alive at times with rats and mice, neither of us had succeeded in getting one.

" You know, Tim," I said, " I don't think you like catching them. You're like me. When I find a trap empty I feel quite relieved."

Tim nodded. "Same here. Before you came, Romany, I could kill owt, but somehow it's different now. What are you laughing at? "

" I'm laughing at the way all your cats are avoiding you. They've never taken their eyes off you since you came through that gate. They usually sit lazily in the sun taking no notice of us. What have you been doing to them ?"

It was Tim's turn to laugh. " Whenever I saw a cat carrying a mouse I chased it and tried to make it drop it. But they're that artful. As soon as I got near one it picked the mouse up and away, it went. Ginger got a young rat this morning and I stalked him for half an hour, but he ran off into the orchard with it."

One evening a few weeks later we met in the Dutch barn as arranged. I was turning round to see where Raq was when I heard a hiss and the unmistakable spit of a cat, and then saw Raq chasing it with a yelp of delight.

The next moment Tim dived to the ground and came up holding the warm body of a mouse by the tail.

" At last! " he gasped as I flashed my torch on to it and saw that it was a long-tailed field mouse. Evidently the cat had been returning from the hedge with her victim in her mouth when she had heard Tim and me in the barn.

She turned back and came suddenly face to face with Raq. She dropped the mouse in her surprise and spat viciously at him. When Raq returned from the chase we could see him with his nose down, picking up our trail until it led him to the hay in the Dutch barn.

Tim patted him. " Thanks for your help, old man."

Raq did not understand him, but from the furious wagging of his tail we could see that he knew that he was in high favour.

Though Spring had only officially arrived the day before, the weather was mild as we lay on the hay awaiting Spook's appearance. Though she kept us waiting, the time passed quickly as we listened to the various sounds outside.

" It's good to hear that sound again, Tim," I said as the notes of some curlews rang out high above us. These birds live all the winter on the seashore or on the mudflats in our estuaries, and return to make their nests on our moor lands in Spring.

" They're migrating," I said as we peered out, trying to catch sight of them in the darkness. " There may be a hundred or more of them. That first call was the leader asking whether all was well, or it may have been a rallying call to keep the flock from wandering. Did you hear that second note-the answering call of a bird in the rear 'All is well' ?

" I like almost every bird call, but I would rather miss any of them than the lonesome piping of the curlew."

Tim brought me back to earth by saying, " Hear that peewit, Romany?"

" Yes, and that moorhen on the pond. You can't mistake her ' Croot-Croot,' can you ?"

" Oh, there goes Honk," he cried.

Tim was right. Near the riverside we could hear the clank of a heron as he flew to his roost, perhaps with a well-filled crop after a successful fishing expedition. We listened to various bird calls, squeaks from the inky bottom of the hedge and rustlings somewhere below us in the hay. Tim knew the name of each dog that we heard barking in neighbouring farms. He would say:

" That's Bob Baxter's Peter, or Sam Gill's Bluster."

We were lying very still trying to identify a slight scratching sound which came from the wood when Tim nudged my arm. " Here comes spook," he whispered.

She waited by so close to us that we could see her lovely wings very clearly. In width they seemed twice as long as her body. Tim put his fingers in his ears and waited for her to screech, but no sound came.

" Perhaps she's not giving the game away to-night. She must be hungry," I said.

" Do you mean that her scream frightens mice and rats away," Tim inquired.

" If I were a mouse and I heard that screech I should squat where I was and never blink an eyelid. Some people say that an owl never screeches when hungry, but we've heard Spook screeching before she began hunting, haven't we? " Tim agreed.

I peered out in the direction of the wood. There was sufficient light for me to see its dark outline, and I could pick out several individual trees not far away. From the distance came a screech and looking out we had the luck to see Spook a few minutes later fly back and perch on one of the trees close to the barn.

Tim seemed fascinated by her big eyes. We were so close to her that they looked like two big car head lamps.

I reminded him that owls' eyes are specially adapted for using at night-so made as to use every scrap of light. I got out my binoculars and showed him what big lenses they had, and reminded him of the powerful camera lens I always use when taking photographs of a bird in deep shadow. " We've learnt how to make these lenses by studying the eyes of night-hunting birds, Tim."

Meanwhile Spook was standing like a statue, peering down into the grass below her. Then came a screech, and the next moment she dived as silently as a ghost.

Floating along at great speed for a few yards, she seemed to pull herself up in mid-air, turn round in her own length, and dive like an arrow to the ground. There followed a piteous squeal from the grass, loud at first and trailing pathetically away. Then all was still again.

Spook, with her talons fixed in her victim, never moved an inch.

" Another rat gone west," said Tim with satisfaction.

" She screeched to frighten him, and she made him so nervous that he showed where he was hiding. Look! There she goes."

" Aye. And she's carrying it in her talons, not her beak."

The night darkened considerably, so we were not able to tell where Spook took her prey, but she seemed to be going in the direction of her own barn.

" Why did she stay down on the ground so long after she'd struck the rat? " was Tim's next question.

I told him that she killed it by digging her talons deeper and deeper into the rat's body-not a very pleasant thought. A sparrow hawk dashes at a bird, grips it in its talons, and carries it off to some killing mount, and then raps it at the base of its skull.

" And is the bird in pain all the time ? " he asked with concern.

" No. I picked up a bird that a hawk had dropped the other day, and found it quite unharmed. That's unusual, of course. I believe they generally become unconscious and know nothing about it."

" Like our Dick when he had that crash with his motor bike. He couldn't remember a thing that had happened."

We waited on, hoping that Spook would come out again to hunt, but we saw no sign of her. Then Mrs. Fletcher's voice rang out from the kitchen telling Tim that his supper was ready, and that he was to bring Mr. Romany in with him. Tim picked up his specimen mouse and followed me down into the stack yard.

THE RAT SQUEALS TWICE

I AM afraid I left to Tim the job of putting the dead body of the mouse into the solution he had prepared, especially as it was one of those harmless little long-tailed field-mice of which I am very fond. Had it been hot weather we could have got these specimens without all this bother. Tim had several guesses before I had to tell him what I meant by this statement.

" We should only have to put the mouse in a sunny spot and leave the bluebottles to do the rest."

Tim laughed. " Gosh, Romany! I never thought of it."

I explained how useful bluebottles are in cleaning up millions of dead creatures every year which otherwise would lie and rot in the fields, causing disease.

" They always lay their eggs on decaying matter, because their maggots need it to feed on."

Tim looked a bit dubious. " Aye, that's all right, but they lay their eggs on our meat and bacon an' all."

" That's because you don't keep it covered up. How can a bluebottle tell the difference between a dead rabbit in the fields and a dead rabbit hanging up in your larder ?"

All he says is: 'Hullo! Here's a fine nest for my eggs. When they hatch out my grubs will find their food all around them."

We compared the little field-mouse with other kinds of mice - house-mouse, the red-backed meadow-mouse, the short-tailed mouse, and the harvest-mouse which makes its nest in the standing corn, and we decided to watch the habits of long-tail when we had time.

" It won't be an easy job, Tim," I said. " He's so tiny. When I've tried to find him I've wasted a lot of time. Then suddenly he has popped up accidentally just when I was not expecting him."

The following night I was awakened by an unusually loud noise. Not wanting to disturb Raq, who was curled up against me, I half sat up in bed and listened. It was Spook screeching more loudly than ever.

It was a beautiful moonlit night, so I decided to get dressed and go out and investigate. Once he was awake, Raq was just as ready for a walk as though it had been midday. I told him, however, that he would have to keep strictly to my heel and not run off on his own.

I crossed the lane, intending to keep on the path that skirted the edge of the wood, so that I should be hidden by the trees and yet be able to see the open fields on my left.

Everything was very still, except for a rabbit that scurried away just in front of me which Raq badly wanted to chase, and a wren who scolded me sharply for disturbing her sleep. Against the light of the moon I could see the male rooks sitting near the large black nests on which their mates were broodily sitting.

" Keep still, old man," I said. I had heard the sound of grunting and snuffling under some bramble bushes in front of us. Fortunately the breeze was not blowing our scent towards the night-prowler, so the grunting and snuffling came nearer and nearer, until a little snout appeared and we saw that it was a hedgehog on the hunt.

Most night-hunters are very stealthy in their movements, but hedgehogs don't seem to care how noisy they are.

Perhaps they know that they have such a spiky suit of armour that few enemies will attack them. As the hedgehog came out from behind the bush he pushed his nose into every tuft of grass, and turned over every stone to see if there were any beetles lurking beneath. So intent was he on getting a good supper that he never knewthat Raq and I were barely two feet away from him.

Before we left him he came across a lucky find in the ditch-a dead young bird-and we could hear him slicing it with his sharp teeth.

When we got near the pond I was surprised to hear excited sounds coming from the moorhens nesting there.

I felt sure that it was not due to our presence, because we had been careful not to make any disturbing sounds. So I crept along cautiously, manoeuvring round the pond so that the moonlight lit up both the banks and gave me a good view. Mrs. Moorhen was standing on a large stone on which her nest rested, and was peering into the water in a very agitated manner. Backwards and forwards she wagged her head and long neck, at the same time uttering pathetic cries for help.

Suddenly a rush along the bank betrayed the where-abouts of her mate, who had come to her rescue. Then it was that I saw ripples on the water and realised that the enemy was a rat who was intent on raiding the nest, knowing well what a tasty dish moorhens' eggs make.

Meanwhile the cock bird without hesitation half flew and half swam across the pond to attack the enemy.

With his long legs he tried to kick him, and with his bill he tried to jab him; but the rat was an expert swimmer, and he dived under the water. Both moorhens were puzzled and worried. Surface raiders they were accustomed to dealing with, but this living submarine was another matter altogether.

Finally the cock decided to get up on the boulder and help his mate to guard the nest. When the rat came up they both attacked him together. He dived once more and this time came up on the opposite side of the nest and had just managed to get his feet on the stone when the moorhens spotted him and literally flung themselves at him. It was at this moment that Raq thought it about time that he should join in the fray. He is not fond of rat-hunting but he does love chasing moorhens.

He made one rush into the pond. The rat caught sight of him and beat a hasty retreat, whilst the moorhens flew to the bank, leaving the nest unguarded. I whistled Raq to come to heel. He came at once, knowing that he had done wrong in taking French leave, and fearing that I should be cross with him; but I was too busy watching the ripples on the water as the rat made off to the end of the pond and then scrambled up the bank.

We hurried round the pond edge, and as the moonlight fell on a path leading from the water to the wood, to my surprise we saw the wet bedraggled-looking rat limping along twenty yards ahead of us, with his long tail slithering behind in the mud. The moorhen must have caught him a blow after all. Suddenly there came a bolt from the blue. From a tree above him something swooped down.

He never heard it; in fact he knew nothing until Spook's sharp talons got him in such a grip that he could neither bite nor even wriggle. He looked up into the merciless unexpressionless eyes of the owl, and then let out a squeal that made every other rat abroad crouch down and give thanks that it wasn't himself. The rat squealed again, this time a faint echo of his first alarm. Meanwhile I was watching Spook. She never moved an inch. So still was she that she might have been posing for her photograph in that moonlit glade. Not until she had squeezed the very life out of her victim did she stretch out her wings and fly noiselessly towards the farm.

" It served him right. He shouldn't have tried to rob the moorhens' nest," I said to Raq as we followed Spook towards the farm.

Remembering what Tim had told me, I kept my eyes open as I neared the buildings to see whether any fox might be on the prowl. Turning one dark comer I unfortunately knocked against a bucket. This brought a growl from Sam, one of the farm dogs, which soon died down when he got our scent. A window opened and Fletcher's voice came from above in gruff tones, " Who's there? "

" It's only, Romany," I said quietly. " I thought the fox might be about."

"I thought as much when Sam barked," he replied, Good-night "-and he closed the window.

Walking past Spook's barn I happened to glance casually across at the field beyond it, and got a lovely surprise. Not only was Spook there, sailing over the field with airy grace, but she had a mate with her for the first time, and they seemed to be playing together.

It was their combined screeching that had wakened me from my sleep. This was news for Tim. I got out a scrap of paper and a pencil from my pocket, and against the stable door I wrote: " Spook has a mate. I've seen them together. That means owlets. Hooray ! Romany."

Behind the Dutch barn was a big water-tub raised from the ground by four bricks. Under the tub was a tin, and in this I placed my note for Tim. It was our secret post-box. Instead of leaving messages for me with his mother or father, he dropped them in the tin, and I did the same.

I should like to have tapped on his bedroom window and let him see Spook and her mate for himself, but I thought that it would spoil his night's sleep.

As I walked back towards the vardo I went a few yards out of my way to see how the moorhens were faring.

Mrs. Moorhen's black form could be seen sitting like a lid on top of her shadowed nest. Mr. Moorhen would be somewhere on the bank, sleeping with one ear and one eye open. I did not catch sight of him, but from the way Raq pointed with his nose towards a bed of reeds under some willow trees I think he was probably in there.

As I settled down to sleep I was conscious of a screech away in the distance, and I remember thinking that, though I could never live with anyone who had such a voice, to an owl it must be the sweetest sound imaginable.

RAQ DISCOVERS BROWNIE'S NEST

TIM was overjoyed to read my news, and the following night he persuaded his mother to let him stay up late. When he caught sight of the two owls floating together over the dusky fields he was so excited that he could hardly stop turning cartwheels on the grass. Raq looked surprised at his enthusiasm. He was frankly bored with the whole proceeding. He seemed to be saying,

"I don't know what you see in these dull old owls. Give me something I can chase or something I can scent."

We went up frequently to the barn, and sometimes they did not even turn their heads to look at us, though we now had our hide fixed within a few yards of them.

Tim confided in me that his mother had said that she was surprised that none of her chickens or ducklings was missing. I told him that I did not think there was any fear of this unless there was a real scarcity of the owls' natural food. If hungry, they naturally eat whatever they can find.

Tim thought for a moment. " I shall tell her that they do more than pay for losing a few chickens because they eat our mice and rats." The owls had found a champion in Tim.

" Many people make the mistake of thinking that because one bird suddenly turns on poultry or gamechicks all birds of that kind do the same. Because one kestrel takes a few pheasant chicks when they happen to be near, it does not mean that all kestrels are game stealers. You know, Tim, how a sheep-dog that tends sheep all day long sometimes becomes a sheep-killer at night. But that doesn't mean that all sheep-dogs are sheep-killers."

Tim agreed, and reminded me how we had once made a test with half a dozen hedgehogs, and had found that some of them would not look at an egg which we placed in their way, whilst others ate it greedily.

The next morning when I visited the farm Tim was busy helping his father in the fields, so I left him a note that I would meet him in the barn at dinner time.

" What shall we call Spook's mate, Romany? " he asked as he flopped down on the hay beside me.

" What about Wraith? " I asked

He looked a bit dubious, but when I explained that it meant a ghost he nodded his head.

It was at that moment that one of the owls suddenly took it into its head to fly outside in broad daylight. We heard no screech, but saw it fly past the byre and settle on the branch of an ash tree at the fringe of the wood.

"By gosh ! " said Tim. "In broad daylight ! I wonder what she's up to." We both scrutinised the owl near us. Wraith and Spook were so very alike in appearance that in the dark rafters of the barn it was difficult to tell " t'other from which" , as Tim put it. So I got out my field glasses and focused them on the distant bird.

" It's Wraith. If you look carefully you'll see that the mottled marks on Spook's breast are bigger than his, and I also think his back is a little lighter buff than hers."

I passed the glasses to Tim, and was just telling him to notice particularly the delicate white feathering around each eye, when we heard the shriek of a blackbird.

" Chink-Chink-Chink " came the angry, excited call.

" You know what that means, Tim? She's just seen Wraith up there."

It seemed as though the blackbird's alarm had wakened every small bird in the neighbourhood, for wrens, chaffinches, linnets, hedge-sparrows and tits appeared from all directions, and we could see them flying in and out of the nearby trees, and shrieking out the most unpleasant things at the top of their voices.

Tim laughed. " Wraith doesn't seem to be minding."

It was true. The owl appeared to be quite unperturbed by their clamour. So far as we could see, no bird actually attacked him, but they certainly destroyed what he hoped would have been a quiet few minutes. The small birds looked like a lot of flies buzzing round him. He bore it as long as he could. Then he launched himself into the air, and was followed by a bird or two for a few yards; but when he reached the barn he was alone, and the wood became silent once more.

"I've seen birds chase a hawk, but not an owl before, Tim remarked. " I've seen them make a fox move on by doing that, too. " Yes. And did you notice that Wraith managed to fly quite well ? Some people think that owls cannot see in the daylight. They can, but of course they are happier in the dark."

" It's queer how they can see in pitch darkness, isn't it, Romany ? "

" They can't," I said. " But there are not many nights so dark that even we can not see the shape of anything, and our eyes are not made for night-hunting. There are few nights when owls, foxes and nightjars can't see well enough to be able to hunt for their supper."

"You're right. When Dad and I come out late at night sometimes to see that the stock are all right, I can't see a blessed thing; but after a minute or two I'm all right."

On the cobbles outside we could hear the feet of the men getting ready to start work again, so we made our way down the steps.

" What made Wraith suddenly take it into his head to fly in daylight? " Tim asked.

" That is a difficult question. But personally I think he was just letting off steam."

I explained that it would not be long before Spook laid her eggs, and that all birds enjoyed having a family, so perhaps Wraith was feeling a bit excited about it all.

"You've seen other birds do it-the plover diving and swerving, the raven turning over on his back in mid-air, the wood pigeon soaring up on outstretched wings."

As I turned to take the path through the wood to the vardo I heard the alarm call of a hen in the orchard.

Thinking that a rat might be attacking her chickens, I turned aside. The hen was in her coop with her young brood around her. She was pushing her head through the wooden bars and gazing upward in alarm. Looking up, I saw a carrion crow change its course, having seen me come into the orchard.

" Good old sentinel," I said to her.

A few weeks previously she had been an ordinary silly greedy old hen, frightened of her very shadow. But the coming of those fluffy chicks had transformed her and now she had become alert to every danger that threatened them.

She would face a dog or a rat. She was no longer greedy, either. She would scratch up insects for them, and never touch the food Mrs. Fletcher brought for them until they were satisfied.

When Raq went near her she clucked to her brood to run for shelter, and fluffed out her feathers to make herself look as big and fierce as possible. When we left her she was protecting her chirping youngsters, at the same time pushing her head through the coop to watch for enemies.

The wood was beautiful in its new green dress. The chestnut buds had burst from their sticky wrappings and were opening out their long angers. The emerald-green skirts of the larch trees swayed gracefully in the breeze, but the backward oak and ash trees looked bare, though their bases were carpeted with bluebell spikes. One bole was surrounded with great clusters of primroses.

Hearing the tapping of a woodpecker in the distance, and thinking that I might see him at work, I moved farther into the wood. Unfortunately he heard me coming, and all I saw was a glimpse of his black and white markings and the scarlet on his head and tail. I found that he had been busy working on a decayed silver birch tree.

Meanwhile Raq had found the trail of a pheasant, and with nose to the ground he was following it into a mass of brambles and dead bracken, in the centre of which lay an old tree trunk. One thick branch stuck up a foot or so from the ground, and was so decayed that it was hollowed out like a gun-barrel. When Raq reached it, he stood on his hind legs to investigate it. No sooner did his nose touch the entrance than I heard a hiss, and the next minute a brown bird flew out.

Raq dropped to the ground in fright and turned to look at me as if saying, " Gosh! That gave me a nasty turn."

It gave me a surprise, too, but also pleased me, because I knew that he had discovered the nest of a brown owl.

" More good news for Tim," I said, as I patted him affectionately.

Tim was driving the potato dibbler when I found him. This is a machine which makes holes at regular intervals in which the sprouting potatoes are planted. He pulled up at once when he saw me, and when I told him of Rag's find, he whistled with delight.

" It's in a place I should never have thought of exploring, Tim. It only shows that we mustn't take any place for granted."

" What with Wraith and Spook and now Brownie , we shall have lots more exciting adventures. Get on , Bess, lass," he called as he went on with his job.

" Aye," said Fletcher, when I walked across to speak to him. " him's getting a very useful lad-very useful. He's got his head screwed on the right way."

Before leaving the field I noticed a small patch of earth that I fancied Tim must have overlooked, so when he pulled up again I pointed to it.

" It's all right, Romany. There's a plover's nest there. We didn't want to crush it," he shouted.

" Good lad," I replied, and went over to see it. The eggs were discoloured so I knew that they were nearly ready for hatching, and as they were still warm, I knew that the bird had not been unduly disturbed by the presence of men working in the field.

I had been so interested in the nest that I had not noticed that all this time poor Raq was being dive-bombed.

The cock plover did not object to men working, but a strange dog he would not tolerate, so he swooped down at him again and again until Raq finally ran back to me, looking very wry and woebe-gone.

As I was finishing my tea I heard Tim's footsteps on the vardo steps, and it was not long before we were on our way to look at Brownie's nesting-hole.

" We'd better keep a sharp look out, Tim. You know how fierce brown owls are, and how they dislike strangers." Tim's reply was to break a stick off a nearby ash tree.

However, he did not need to use it because the whole time we were removing the bramble branches which would obstruct our view of the entrance, and preparing a hiding place that we could use from time to time behind some holly bushes, we saw no sign whatever of Brownie.

We then walked through the wood and climbed slowly towards the moors. The willow-warblers who had just returned from Africa were singing incessantly, but I preferred the soft crooning of the wood-pigeons in the distant wood.

" There's our friend, the wheatear, back in his old haunts again," I said, as a grey and black bird flitted by showing a conspicuous white patch above his tail.

" He's the beggar who dodged in and out of the big stones, isn't he ? " Tim remarked.

" Yes. He has often deceived me for hours doing that when I've been searching for his nest."

We sat down for a while to enjoy the view below us.

" The country would not be half so picturesque without farms like yours, Tim," I said, and I pointed out to him the patchwork of colour-the blue-green oats, the sea-green wheat, the silvery green of the young barley, the rich darker green of the meadows, and the purple-brown earth of the ploughed fields.

" If there were no farms the land would be all swamps and jungle. Your father not only produces food, but helps to make the countryside beautiful."

Tim's eyes lit up. " I'll remember that when I'm a farmer, Romany," he said.

TIM IS ATTACKED

LOOKING out of the vardo window whilst I was having breakfast a few mornings later, I saw Tim running up the woodland path.

" I can't stay, Romany, but Spook's got two eggs," he cried breathlessly. " She's laid them on the floor of the barn and is sitting on them."

Just to see how observant he was I asked him whether she had made any kind of a nest.

He shook his head. " Not so far as I could see. She's sitting in a heap of her own pellets. She looked as proud as Punch."

" Keep your eyes open for any partridges," I called after him as he ran off to help his father roll a field of oats, accompanied along the path for a short distance by Raq.

For several evenings we visited the barn for a short time to see what was happening. Only two eggs were laid during the first week, and when Spook flew off the nest I showed Tim that they were neither as round nor as glossy as those of the brown owl.

" How long will she sit ? " Tim asked.

"About a month on those two," I replied.

On our next visit there were three eggs. Tim whistled.

" But those first two eggs will have a week's start, Romany."

I explained that owls are not like ordinary birds which lay one egg each day till their full clutch is laid before starting to brood.

" We shall see both the young owls and the eggs in this nest at the same time."

In between we paid a visit to Brownie, and were relieved to find that she did not appear to resent our presence very much. At least, Tim had no occasion to use his stick.

We flashed a torch down the hollow tree trunk and found two white eggs and two very young birds which seemed to be covered with grey fluffy wool. While Tim peered in I kept an eye on Brownie who had just flown into a nearby tree and was watching us keenly, crying out

" Ke-Vick-Ke-Vick."

" She's got a lot more feathers on her legs than Spook has," said Tim. " What's that in her mouth ?"

" It looks like a field-mouse. No, it's a vole. See its blunt nose and short tail."

" Dad says they do a lot of damage to our grass."

" That's true, and your mother will have to watch her young chickens carefully now, because Brownie is not particular what she catches if her youngsters are hungry. You might tell her from me to move her hen-coops nearer the house."

We pretended that we were going into the wood, and then crept quietly back behind the screen of hollies.

Brownie was still sitting on the branch holding the vole.

After a while, hearing nothing that spelt danger, she floated down to the entrance of the hole and, without stopping to perch anywhere, alighted inside it.

"That was clever flying, wasn't it, Tim? Did you notice how she checked her speed before entering?"

We waited for some time hoping that she might , come out to hunt again, but there was no sign of her. Possibly she had been taking a few minutes' respite to stretch her limbs, and had come across the vole by chance while flying over the fields.

On our way home Tim asked me which of the owls I liked best, and I replied without hesitation that I preferred the barn owls. He did, too.

" They seem more friendly-like than the brown uns, and don't make a fuss when we come near them. I like to see Wraith sitting like a statue on the ledge, and Spook on her nest below, just as quiet."

In time Spook laid four eggs altogether and Brownie four, and though Spook's youngsters looked like balls of white fluffy down, they had faces like old men.

" They look like little Esquimaux in their white furs," Tim remarked.

The eggs hatched out in time and we noticed that Spook did not seem to mind leaving the unhatched eggs for long periods once her first two babies had been hatched.

I explained to Tim that the young birds kept the eggs warm while the mother bird was away on the hunt for food.

" Aye. She leaves two hot-water bottles in the nest for them," he remarked.

They were not unlike bulging hot-water bottles, either.

They looked very comical as they sat up in the nest with their legs stretched out in front of them and their tummies bulging with mice and other rodents.

We spent far more time in the barn with Spook And Wraith than in watching Brownie. Perhaps it was because we had more comfortable quarters and a much better view of the young birds.

During the day the youngsters sat in the nest, sometimes with their mother and sometimes alone.

"Why doesn't Wraith take a turn on the nest, Romany ? " Tim asked one day as we were sitting in our hide.

" I don't know, Tim. Perhaps he does, though I've never seen him do it. A gamekeeper once told me that he had seen the male bird incubating the eggs."

We found it very difficult to see whether the parents tore the mice into shreds to feed the owlets when they were first hatched. Spook and Wraith flew in so noise-lessly and so quickly, and the barn was so badly lighted, that the food was eaten before we could see whether it had been carved up for them.

" Hawks you know, Tim," I said, " always stand on top of their victims and tear them to bits before they give them to their newly-hatched youngsters. These owls crush them to pulp so that they can be swallowed easily."

What amazed us most was the early age at which the owlets dealt with a whole mouse themselves- and what enormous appetites they had !

One evening the hunting must have been especially good, because the parent birds kept coming in very regularly with food.

" Look, Romany. That one has a worm hanging out of its mouth."

" Look again," I said, laughing.

" Gosh," said the boy," it's the tail of a mouse. It wont go in. He's so full up."

This was true. The owlet had eaten so many mice that he couldn't swallow it.

The young bird sat quite still with its eyes closed until we saw the tail slowly disappearing.

We could not understand why one of the eggs was so long hatching out. On investigation we found that it had a tiny hole in the shell-probably made by the talons of one of the owlets.

It was a great sight to see the youngsters of different ages sitting together, all making most curious noises.

When they were angry they made a snapping noise with their bills. At other times they hissed like snakes or snored like hedgehogs.

" It's lucky for the younger birds that there are plenty of mice and young rats and voles about," I said.

" Do you mean that they would die of hunger ? " he asked.

" No. But when owls nest in March and the weather is so cold that mice are kept indoors, the bigger birds in the nest sometimes eat the smaller ones."

" Cruel beggars," Tim blurted out.

" Yes, but imagine the big ones ravenous with hunger, Tim. Why should they die as well as the little ones ? "

I reminded him that whereas we humans concentrate our energies on saving the individual, the instinct of birds and insects seems to be not to let their race die out.

Though a whole colony of wasps die in the autumn, the queen wasp is guarded and tended so that she may be kept alive to produce a new family the next spring.

Bees when ill will creep away from their fellows to die so that disease shall not spread through the hive. Sick animals do the same thing.

" You've seen the house martins under the eaves of your farm, Tim. If they happen to nest late, and cold weather comes, they leave the youngsters to their fate and fly south themselves. It seems cruel to us, I know."

The owlets were very fascinating to watch, with their quaint, wise expressions ; and the curious noises they made reminded me to tell Tim how one of the farm hands at Whitrigg Farm went into the stable late one night to tend a sick horse, and heard such a queer snoring noise that be fetched the farmer and told him that a tramp was asleep up in the hay-loft. They took their storm-lamps and climbed the ladder, and their surprise can be imagined when all they found were young barn owls. Tim had not heard this story before.

He then asked why the young owlets had soft fluffy down, and were not born with feathers like their parents.

He got the answer when he watched the youngsters tackling some mice covered with blood. " If they had feathers they would get so dirty that when the time came for them to leave the nest they would not be able to fly. Then, too, down is much warmer and cosier, and takes less room in the nest." As the owlets grew bigger we watched the soft fluff gradually fall off, leaving feathers ready for flight.

The young owls seemed so tame that one day Tim thought it would be an easy job to reach a few pellets out of the nest. I was watching Spook at the time, when suddenly I heard Tim shout " Ow ! " Looking round, I saw that the biggest of the family had gripped Tim's hand.

" Don't move," I shouted as I threw my handkerchief over the bird's head and carefully pulled out the talons.

The other birds had also attacked him, but fortunately they had gripped his coat sleeve. Tim made very little fuss, considering the pain he must have suffered. It was fortunate that we were so near the farm. As she applied the iodine and bandaged his hand up, Mrs. Fletcher showed far more concern than he did.

" If that is how he grips a mouse I shall feel more sorry for them in future," Tim remarked.

" You will, but his grip is so swift and sudden that they don't suffer long. It's over very quickly."

In our spare time we had experimented with our dead specimens with the object of identifying the bones found in the pellets. Unfortunately it was not a great success.

In the first place, lime had not been really satisfactory, and the smell was so vile that neither Tim nor I could endure it. We then tried using caustic soda, but this was too slow.

Finally I had a brain-wave. We took the specimens, placed then on an ant-hill, and let the ants do the job for us. When they had cleaned them they were as white as marble. Even then it wasn't easy to compare them with the bones found in the pellets. The latter were so small and broken that it was difficult to tell which was which. However, we learned and marvelled a good deal during our investigations.

The last time we saw the owlets will always remain in our minds. Tim and I were returning at dusk from a walk on the moors when in the field near the barn we saw four white forms floating above the grass. We stopped to watch them, entranced by their quiet move-ment. Then both Spook and Wraith joined them, and they flew on together over the fields, making a charming picture.

" It looks as though the parents are giving them a lesson on how to catch mice," I said.

At times the young birds seemed to get tired of their lessons and they started to play. As they flew around, there was none of the reckless dash of the hawk, but they could turn easily and dive to the ground as surely if not as swiftly as some birds do. Their screeches were very eerie, especially when they flew close to our hiding place.

" I shan't put my head under the bedclothes any more when I hear them screeching," Tim said, laughing.

" No, Tim. It is the unknown which makes us afraid."

As their airy forms vanished into the darkness we made our way back to the farm, loth to take our leave of these birds which had given us so much pleasure.

We went up to the barn later that evening and found

Spook and Wraith up on the rafters having a nap, but there was no sign of the owlets.

" I suppose they've gone to find good hunting fields for themselves," said Tim.

" Yes, Spook and Wraith have done their job. They've reared a healthy strong family, able to look after themselves. They well deserve a rest."

FARM HORSES

As Raq and I turned towards the open country, in nine out of every ten houses the blinds were still drawn.

" They're all missing the best part of the day, old man, aren't they?" I said to him. For answer he jumped up and touched my fingers with his velvet nose.

The sun was brilliant, and on every field were the long shadows of the trees. How cool their delicate lace-work looked as it fell on the grass !

A delicious fragrance arose from a new-mown field as the dew lay on the long swathes. The birds were busy hopping about picking out the insects which swarmed on their stems.

High in the air the swifts wheeled and screamed.

I have watched these black-coated migrants foryears, but they are still strangers to me. The swallow and the house-martin love to swerve near the haunts of man, and seem ever ready to be friendly with him. Not so the swifts. There is no friendship with them. They live apart, never seeming to sleep, never beholden to any man.

Passing a hole in a tree well known to me, I noticed that a blue-tit had hatched her young family and that the nest was discarded. There had been eleven fluffy mites in it-a sheer case of over-crowding. How they had all managed to breathe is beyond me, for they lay in tiers, and what the bottom row must have endured during the recent hot weather is beyond imagination. What an upheaval took place each time the parent bird returnedwith food! Those at the bottom forced their way to the top, with open bills. Each return must have caused a miniature earthquake in the nest.

Searching about, I discovered them-little atoms of grey-green, blue and yellow, seated two by two on the branches of a hawthorn. For a time they snuggled down, finding difficulty in keeping their balance, for their 'rudders' were not developed. Then, as they caught sight of the mother-bird returning, there was wild excitement and a fluttering of tiny wings. Each duly received his share of food , though how the mother managed to carry a bit for each was incredible. And how she remembered who had had their share was likewise a mystery, so like each other were they.

Raq loves the farm, and when I turned up the lane which leads to it, he showed great delight.

Joe was in the stable with the lads, who were brushing down the horses before turning them out. It is best done when the horses are dry, to get that lovely sheen which makes them shine like silk.

" How often are they fed ? " I asked.

" Three times a day-a bit of hay, some rolled oats, and bran," replied Joe.

Magnificent animals they looked, so suggestive of power. A bull gives me the sense of tremendous strength, but a horse gives me the sense of beauty - also curved strength.

" I do love to see them rolling over on their backs in the field, Joe."

Joe smiled. "Aye, and it's good for 'em an' all. When they've bin workin' an' are turned loose they're ready a'most to begin again if they have a roll. It kind o' relaxes all their muscles and makes 'em fit again."

" Do they lie down when they sleep ?"

Joe nodded. " Most on 'em does."

" You find odd uns though, that sleep standing up, don't you, Joe ? " said John, who had just come into the stable.

" Do they stand on all fours ? " I asked.

They both laughed at this. "Aye, they do," said

Joe. " But they tires easily, and their sleep can't do 'em much good. If I bought a horse at a sale, and then found later that 'e went to sleep standin' up, I should return 'im to the feller as sold 'im to me, and he'd have to take him back. We reckons it a fault in a horse, ye see."

" Have you noticed that a horse gets up different from a cow ? " John asked.

Glad to show that I knew a little, I said, " Yes, a horse rises by straightening out its fore-legs first, and a cow straightens out its hind legs first."

Joe laughed. "There's a good many as couldn't tell ye that, I reckon."

As we left the stable the dogs began to bark, and Sally, Joe's wife, appeared at the back door. It was Ned arriving with the letters, so we all gathered round as he dipped into his bag.

"Not much this mornin'," he said apologetically to Sally.

" Ned,' I said, "what's the difference between the way a horse gets up after lying down and the way a cow gets up ? "

The old postman chuckled. "Is that a riddle, or do ye really want to know ? " he asked. Then, seeing by the smiles that I was having a bit of fun, he said, "Tell me first, 'ow can ye tell 'ow old a horse is ?"

"By looking at its teeth," I replied promptly.

Joe put his hand on my shoulder and said, "Good fer you. That's reet."

"An' 'ow can ye tell the age of a chicken ?" Ned persisted.

" By chewing it," said Joe, much to everyone's amusement.

" By looking at its legs ,and examining the scales on them," said Sally.

Ned nodded. "An'how can ye tell the age of a tree ? "

"By the rings on the cross-section of its trunk," answered John.

Again Ned nodded. "Now I'll ask ye a 'ard one. 'Ow can ye tell the age of a fish ?"

Dead silence.

"By its size," I began.

Ned shook his head. " I were sittin' on t' river bank t' other day, an' a chap fishin' were cuttin' open a fish 'e'd caught. After we'd chatted a bit aboot state o' t' watter, 'e showed me a small stone.

" Know what it is? " he asked. " Nay," says I, " I don't." " It's a otholith," he said, with the look of satisfaction Ned always showed in using long words.

" A otholith," the old postman repeated, and fumbling in his pockets he produced a bit of paper. " I got 'im to write it fer me."

" Well, what is it ? " asked Joe.

" It's a stone oot o'the ear of a fish, which wobbles aboot an'tells t'fish whether it is swinimin' right way up or wrong way up-a kind o' balancer, ye see. Well now, accordin' to t'size of t'stone so ye can tell the age o't' fish."

" Well, I've learned something , this morning," said Sally, with a smile.

" And how do ye tell the age of a woman ? " asked Joe , looking slyly at his wife's receding figure.

Ned looked round, then gave one of his driest chuckles. "I reckon there's only one sure way these days-'er birth certificate."

"Just when lamb becomes mutton tak's some decidin'," said Joe, as Ned departed, and we all followed into the kitchen.

"And what's your job to-day, Joe ?" I asked. He looked up towards the High Barn, scorched with sunshine.

" Scufflin' turnips."

" You are welcome to it," I said, thinking of the heat, the dry earth, and the unending rows of small plants to be thinned out. "How are they looking ?"

" Might be better. T'fly 'as gone wi' some on em. Some say the linnets have bothered 'em."

" Linnets ? " I exclaimed in amazement. "I've never heard of such a thing."

" Well," said Joe, "they're sayin' roond here that linnets have come doon in flocks and taken away t' seed. If it's true, that's a new enemy we have to watch."

" Have you had to sow some again ?"

"Aye, a few, but turnips of a second sowing never do as well as a first."

As I sat in tlie kitchen and watched Joe and his men get ready for their work and heard their hearty fun and chatter, while Sally filled their bottles with tea for their ten-o'clocks, and then saw them turn their faces towards High Barn, I could not help feeling that were I given the choice between a City office and going with them up to High Barn, I should choose the latter.

KEEPER AND POACHER

" THE birds are gathering into flocks," said John Fell as Raq and I walked with him across tlie fields.

" That's a sure sign that sunny days are comin' to an end."

We were tramping through a stubble field and he pointed to the numbers of small birds of the finch variety that took refuge in the hedges at our approach. " Linnets, goldfinches, chaffinches, most on 'em are," said he. We saw them descend to feed on the seeds-the goldfinches looking like drops of sparkling sunshine and red fire as they searched the towsled heads of the thistles.

"They are not communal birds then ? " I asked.

The gamekeeper shook his head. "The nestin' season finds 'em living their own little lives wi' their mates. " Each family fer itsel' " is their motter.

But when the autumn begins to touch every leaf wi' yaller and scarlet, then they join up i' bands, and feed together through the winter."

For a moment or two we watched the little companies. Not for long did any of them settle on the ground. Each moment some alarm or menace would send them like a fluttering cascade to the safety of the hollies and hawthorns. Many of them swayed from the top most branches, where they could be seen surveying the land for the peril that lurked in the shadows.

"Jerry was telling me," I said to John, "that many birds and beasts are now scattering their families right and left, driving them away from the old home, and sending them out into the wide world to seek their own fortunes."

The keeper nodded. " That's' true, " said he.

" Fer some time I've heerd the owls kickin' up an awful shindy. They're drivin' the youngsters away in order to find fresh huntin' grounds fer theirsel's.

Food'll grow scarcer as the days shorten. Jerry's right. I reckon."

119

" Then," I persisted, "why do these birds "-here I pointed to score's of finches on the stubble-"do the exact opposite? More mouths mean less food for each." "Well," said he, "I reckon they do it partly fer protection. They've got many enemies on the look oot fer 'em, and they know it. That's the meanin' o' their continual swinging up and doon from hedge to stubble. And when there's a score or two together, it means that there's scores o' eyes and ears on the look-oot, instead o' just one pair. Also, I fancy, that though there are more mouths to fill, yet when they're i' flocks there's more eyes to seek and find-and it's mostly the seed-eaters that gather inter packs."

He opened a gate that led into a field which was dotted with numerous bare bushes.

"Mice, which owls live mostly on, are not as numerous as seeds, and so them old "screechers" have to consarve their supplies by gettin' rid o' youngsters. If ye tak' perticler notice, ye'll see that all the hen chaffinches live by themselves, and all the cocks seek out each other."

"And why do they do that ? " I asked.

" Can't say," said John. " P'raps they think that absence mak's the heart grow fonder. Or p'raps they've got tired o' each other's company and want a change. I sometimes think that it wouldn't be a bad plan if we men-folk-"

Then he stopped, and I could see the. twinkle dancing at the back of his eyes. But he never finished his sentence.

" This is what I came to 'ave a look at," said he, pointing to the field which stretched out before us.

Raq was already investigating it, and was paying particular attention to a small patch of ground in the centre.

" That's where the partridges jugged last night," said John, watching the dog, who was puzzled by the fact, that though the scent was strong on their camping site, yet he could find no trail leading from it.

" That's 'cos they flew right up and were away wi'oot touchin' t' ground, old man," said John, as he came up to where the dog was casting round for a scent.

"Those bushes," I said to him, "are to prevent poachers, aren't they ?"

" Aye," replied he; "I put 'em in as soon as ever harvest is ovver- If I didn't, a couple o' poachers wi' a good net could sweep the field and bag a whole covey o'partridges as were sleepin' there-they lie so snag an' close."

I went up to one of the bushes. "You don't dig it in then, and fix it firm in the ground ? "

The keeper shook his head. "It gives more trouble to them gentlemen, I reckon, if left loose.

Them thorn bushes get more entangled i' the nets- leastways, that's my experience. "

I looked round the field. " You don't seem to have any regular formation in the placing of the bushes," I said; " they are not spaced out regularly."

" There's a bit o' method, though, i' my madness," John answered with a smile. "If ye'll look roond ye'll see that they're put i' places that are opposite gaps where night prowlers are most likely to come inter t' field. There's that low railin' ovver there, a very likely place fer them night 'awks to pop ovverwell, there's some good spiny hedgehogs waitin' to give the net a welcome. That's the principle I've worked on. "

Once again I looked over the field, and saw that all the weak places were well guarded.

" Generally speaking," I said, "You do not seem to bother much with the parts lying near the hedge."

John shook his head. " Partridges generally snuggle together right i' the middle," he said.

The next field had plenty of natural cover, and Raq was having a great time nosing the rabbits from their seats in the coarse grass and giving chase. Once he got so near to one that his yelp split the air.

" He doesn't often " give mouth," " said the keeper,

" but ye wouldn't have to let him chase rabbits like that if ye used him wi' a gun. If he saw any game in front o' ye, he'd break away and run in and spoil your shot. But ye never use a gun now, do ye ? "

I shook my head. " Never again," I answered.

Seeing scores of little tails bobbing into the hedge bank, I asked, " And why don't you bush this field? There are rabbit poachers as well as game poachers, aren't there ? " John paused to light his pipe." That's true," he said," but it wouldn't be much good bushin'a field to stop rabbit poachin', fer their manner o'usin' the net is different, and ye've got to tak' into accoont that they're after rabbits-which 'as very different habits."

"Ye see," said John, pointing to the warren " when the rabbits first come oot towards dusk they don't run very far away from their burrers. Ye can see how short the grass is cropped near their holes. Then they git more confidence, and want to git oot to the better feed in the middle o' t' field. "

" I can see the lanes they have made in the grass," I said, tracing some of the well-defined pathways that crossed and criss-crossed in front of me.

" Well," continued John, "by ten or eleven o'clock at night all the rabbits are well oot i' the middle there. But it ud be no use fer them fellers to sweep the field as they do when they want to snare the partridge-there's a much better way. Unlike the birds, the rabbits have a definite place o' refuge to mak' fer if disturbed. So the poachers simply stretch their net a few yards from the burrows, parallel to the hedge. Then, when all's ready, they give the word to their dog, and, circlin' the field, the lurcher soon sets the rabbits movin' fer their holes. Scentin' the dog, they race fer their homes, only to dash headlong inter the net. The poachers keep behind the net and move quietly and quickly along as they feel or hear a bunny ' in the toils."

John then picked up an imaginary rabbit by its hind legs and brought his hand down smartly on the back of the neck, indicating the short shrift that the entangled animal received. " Then," he added, " inter the sack it goes."

He shook his head. "No-bush in' a field du be no good fer such work as that."

As John was in a hurry we returned home by the road, instead of the fields, much to Rag's disgust. It was not without interest, for the first thing he found was the poor crushed body of a hedgehog. It was amusing to see how gingerly he sniffed at the carcass, as though he were not sure that even in death the spines might not trouble his nose. Once, in a fit of exuberance, he had touched a hedgehog- but his nose was sore for nearly a week afterwards, and Raq never forgets such experiences.

" Killed by a car," said John disgustedly.

" I have seen quite a number on the roads," said I. " They seem to be getting more numerous."

John shook his head. " It isn't that," said he. " That poor little beggar were trekkin'. I' one way he were migratin' like the birds."

" Migrating ? " I asked with interest.

" Well," said the keeper," he's bin turned oot o' his 'ome. He were born aboot July, and he'd 'ave six or seven brothers and sisters."

" It cannot be particularly comfortable to lie beside an inverted pincushion."

John laughed. " Oh, that's all bin thought oot all right," said he. "When they are born, they come into t' world wi' soft spines-they're not a nest o' young furze-bushes."

" Then," continued the keeper," they've bin looked after wi' great care till just aboot now, when the owd uns know that their bit o' territory 'll feed two on 'em but won't be able to support a big family -so they clear the youngsters oot, with just one thought in their little brains, an' that is to be sure and roll up into a ball when danger threatens. " Curl up, curl up," grunts the mother when any sound comes along that their ear can't uderstand, or her nose can't explain-that's dinned into their ears all day long. "

" So you think he was just setting out to find pastures new when sudden death struck him ? Poor little fellow."

" Aye," said John, "by bad luck he struck the main road soon after leavin' home, and found it easy to travel on. He shuffled along wi'oot meetin' any adventures. P'raps he thought he had found a fine place fer food, fer a lot o' dead things lie on t't road. Then he heard t' sound of the comin' o' a motor and felt t' shake o' t' ground as something rushed towards him. He didn't know what it were, but he remembered his mother's " Curl up, curl up." So he curled up, till speedy death uncurled him for ever."

" Let's give him a decent burial, John," I said.

So we found a rabbit burrow in a quiet spot and placed the little fellow inside, much to Rag's disgust.

RAQ TO THE RESCUE

AS we were having breakfast the next morning Jim popped his head inside the door. " Was that the feller that squealed last night ? " he asked, pointing with his thumb towards the rabbit hanging outside.

" Did you hear it ? " Tim asked.

" Aye. My dogs were that uneasy-like, barkin' all night, I thought there were summat wrong, and when I went out I found that a vixen had been prowlin' around. Then I heard the squeal."

Tim then told him our adventure the previous night.

" But how did you know we were up here ? " Tim went on.

" I saw t' lamp alight when I called at the farm after my supper. You'll be gettin' a telephone put in next," he added with a smile.

" No fear," Tim replied emphatically. " My father would be ringing up when he was short-handed."

" But we could ring your mother up when we were short of food," I suggested.

" That reminds me," Jim interrupted. " Betty sent this." and to our delight, out of his big pockets he brought packet after packet of cakes and pastries, enough to last us for a week.

We then told him about the wild cat that we suspected was hunting in Bluebell Wood, as we called it. Jim nodded. " I had an idea there was one about. I reckon it's that ginger cat belongin' to Joe Crowther. I've noticed him hanging around there once or twice, and was afraid he was leading a double life. If a bit of hard weather comes, I'll have to try and trap him." In reply to Tim's question I explained that the cat would be so cunning that only scarcity of food would entice him to touch the bait in Jim's trap.

While I was frying Jim an extra bit of bacon, Tim asked him about the black-cock we had seen. " You've taken a job on if you're tryin' to watch him," he began.

Then he went on to say that we should have to be up early in the morning to see what he called " them queer carryings-on " when they were pairing up. " I've been on these moors now for nigh on forty years, and I've only seen it twice."

" Tell me about it, " Tim begged; and when he had finished his breakfast, Jim pulled out his twist, lit his pipe, and between long meditative puffs, told his story.

Mentioning the names of a few neighbouring farmers, he told us that one night in March a number of them had been out with their guns, trying to find a dog that had taken to sheep-worrying. They tramped the moors all night without success, and then separated at dawn. " I sat down on the edge of the Dive," he went on, referring to a low cliff about six miles from the Tan, " to have a smoke before makin' my way down again. I remember seeing what I thought were a dog slinkin' up the side of a hedge, but it turned out to be a fox. Then below me something moved in a clearing on the hill-side, and there was a queer sort of ' whirroo ' sound. ' Black-cock,' sez I, and there on a rock were this black feller makin' a din of a row t' first thing in the morning."

He then went on to describe how out of the heather another black-cock appeared. " ' D' you think you're the only pebble on the beach ? 'he cried, strutting up to his rival."

" ' I'll teach you to cheek me,' shrieked the first one, as he drooped his wings and fluffed his feathers out to make himself look as big as possible. For a few minutes they scolded and screamed at each other."

" Was there a fight ? " Tim asked.

" They didn't start that until the spectators arrived."

Then six grey-hens appeared and the two cocks had a 'real set-to. They pecked and scratched one another, and then one of them got hold of toother by his neck, and holdin' him tight he walloped him with his wings until he'd knocked all the stuffm' out of him."

" But he couldn't want all the six grey-hens for himself," Tim said, laughing delightedly at Jim's vivid picture.

" Wait a bit, lad," he went on after re-lighting his pipe with a piece of pinewood from the fire. " A few minutes later two or three more cocks appeared, and they all started going crazy-kickin' their legs up as though they were doin' the can-can. Then I must have scraped my boot against a rock, for when I looked again they were all gone."

He then went on to explain that, unlike grouse and most other birds, black-cocks have more than one mate, and it was usually the best dancer and the best fighter that got the most mates.

Jim then left us to continue his round, and after we had washed up, we tidied up the Tan. We both felt a bit sad that morning, because now that the hay making season was beginning, we were having to leave the Tan for a few weeks to help Mr. Fletcher in the fields.

" There may be a few wet days when we can come up,"

Tim remarked hopefully, as we packed up our haversacks, but in our hearts we knew that the most important thing was that Mr. Fletcher should have a spell of fine hot weather in which to get in all his corn.

Raq had the meal of his life when we emptied the cornbin of the bits and pieces left over, especially as these included one 'of Betty's jam tarts.

While Tim was locking up, I noticed a cock-grouse standing on a boulder by the stream, evidently keeping guard. " Look ! " I whispered to Tim, and he was just in time to see the mother-bird stalk out of the bracken, followed by her family. All the time they were contentedly drinking their fill in the pool, the father remained on guard, looking in all directions in case some enemy should be waiting in the rank grass to pounce on any of his family. Drinking-time is always a dangerous time for birds. Most streams and ponds are surrounded by bushes and herbage, and no one knows better than a fox how easily he can get a meal at such times.

Not until his family were satisfied and had moved off did the cock-grouse feel that it was safe for him to quench his own thirst.

We took the path along the edge of the quarry, hoping to catch a glimpse of the young fox-cubs who would now be well-grown, but we saw nothing of them, and concluded that the family had separated. The youngsters would each be living on their own, and sleeping at night in the scrub-a lonely existence when only a few months old.

" I'll have to tell Ben about that lamb," Tim said, as we looked down on the field where the sheep were grazing.

The lamb was certainly a pathetic object. Not only was it half the size it should have been, but it was hobbling painfully along after its mother. She stupidly did not realise in the least that its foot was damaged, and kept calling it to follow her. Each time it tried to run a few steps we thought it would collapse on the ground from sheer weakness. Still the mother moved on-farther and farther away, and she took no notice whatever of the lamb's cries.

Suddenly a carrion crow alighted on the stone wall not twenty yards from where the lamb was standing.

" We're not the only people that have been watching it," I said as we heard its ominous call.

" Can't we run down and save it ? " Tim asked with concern. I looked round for Raq, but unfortunately he was off hunting, and when I whistled him he did not hear me.

" I'm not so sure that we ought to interfere," I said.

The ewe then called the youngster again, and receiving no reply, she came back this time, much to our relief. But all she did was to smell it to make sure that it was her own lamb, and then walk off again farther and still farther, until she was almost out of sight.

"It looks as though she is deserting it," Tim said angrily, as the ewe went on browsing, taking no notice of her youngster.

" Yes. A sheep never has any patience with a sick lamb," was my reply as we hurried on.

Meanwhile, the crow had been sidling along with a curious crab-like hop nearer and nearer to the lamb.

Then he worked swiftly. He made a lunge at the lamb and drove his beak straight through its head, and before we had realised what had happened he was beginning his meal.

" Look! " Tim cried. " There are three other crows on the wall. How on earth did they know there was food about ? "

" There are few birds with keener sight than carrion crows," I replied. " I think their sense of smell, too, is keener than most birds', but as that lamb was only just killed, I can't believe in this case that they could have scented it."

We neither of us wanted to get a nearer view of the ugly scene, and as I knew that the crow had probably driven his beak through the eye of the lamb, I was not anxious for Tim to see it all. We walked on in silence. Even Raq sensed our depression, and kept at my heel most of the way. As we neared the Tan, Tim said, " Why did you say just now that you weren't sure if we ought to interfere? "

" Because I saw that the lamb was a weakling, and knew that if the crow had not attacked it, it would have become weaker and weaker, and would have had to endure untold suffering before it died a natural death. This would have been far worse than the mercifully quick stab of that crow. Its death was painless and instantaneous, however much it may have sickened us to watch the whole business." As I spoke we could hear the crows quarrelling amongst themselves for the best portions.

" I bet there won't be much of it left by now," Tim remarked.

" Ben wouldn't be very pleased if they did leave any of it," I said, referring to the shepherd, and I explained that blow-flies were the greatest enemy of a flock of sheep in summer, for where there are blow-flies there are maggots, which can soon damage a healthy flock of sheep. I reminded him, too, of the good that all scavengers do, by cleaning up the dead things lying in the fields.

Were this not done by the rats and carrion crows, our walks in the fields would often be spoilt by unpleasant sights and smells.

" You always find something good to say, even about rats and carrion crows," Tim said with a laugh.

" Yes , there's some good even in the worst of them," I replied.

We walked downwards to the vardo by way of Bluebell Wood, hoping that we might see more signs of the wild cat, so that we could report its movements to Jim. When we reached the fields which lay on one side of it, Tim pointed to a kestrel hovering in the air. Fan was on the hunt for food again. Though Raq, too, was hunting along the side of the hedge in the same field, she took no notice of him. It may be that she had seen him with us so often that she thought no danger threatened her. Finding nothing to swoop down at, she then made a sideways flight towards the wood.

Here she stopped and hovered again, making a graceful picture.

Meanwhile Raq had pushed on and had also reached the wood. Suddenly Fan swooped down at something-probably a mouse or a vole that she had spotted on the ground. As she dived quickly downwards we saw her open out her tail to its full extent to check her speed. Then, to our horror, something leapt up at her from the grass.

" It's the wild cat, " shouted Tim excitedly, as we saw the cruel unshielded claws stretched out in a frantic effort to clutch at the kestrel. With a terrified scream, Fan tried to rise in the air , just as the cat struck at her flight feathers.

Then it was that Raq came to the rescue. He let out a joyful yelp, and the cat as it dropped to the ground turned for a second to spit viciously at him. The last we saw of them was the cat rushing into the woods, and Raq some distance behind chasing it at full speed.

We looked at one another without saying, a word, and it was not until we had reached the scene of the incident that Tim said, " I thought Fan was done for, Romany."

" So did I; and I was afraid the cat would turn on Raq, too."

" Good old Raq ! " Tim said affectionately as the dog came rushing towards us. " You saved Fan's life."

Tim was right. Raq had appeared on the scene just in time. The cat must have seen him, because he was standing directly in front of it. It may have been the sight of Raq that made it check its spring-just falling short by an inch of striking Fan with its claws.

Neither of us had noticed what had happened to Fan.

Once we knew that she was out of danger, our eyes had been on Raq.

" Let's go and see if we can find any clues as to where the cat is hiding. When it saw that Raq was so far behind, it probably made for its usual hiding-place."

Tim was a bit puzzled by this, so I explained that if Raq had been right on the cat's tail, it would have jumped up the nearest tree to safety.

We had not gone very far into the wood before we heard Raq again, and I knew by his continuous barking that he had found the cat up a tree. We approached quietly, and found him gazing up into a big oak tree.

Though there was no cat to be seen, the mass of ivy and small branches in the lower fork of the tree looked a very likely hiding place.

" We may have to wait a long time," Tim remarked.

I tiptoed round to the other side of the trunk and examined it carefully. Then I beckoned to Tim. On the bark were the scratchings of scores and scores of claw-marks, beginning a yard and a half from the ground.

" That's enough proof for me," I said, and after patting Raq for his second good deed of the day, we crept away again.

" Are you going to tell Jim? " Tim asked.

" Yes. I'm afraid we must. Wild cats do so much harm to his game-birds. We'll go round to his cottage tonight after supper and tell him."

AN ISLAND NURSERY

A COUPLE of mornings after the cat episode, I walked over to the far end of Fletcher's land to see what I could do to help them. I found Tim driving the mowing machine, and as soon as he saw me he waved joyously.

This was the second welcome I had received, for I had lent my mare to Fletcher for his busy season, and when Comma saw me opening the gate she whinnied loudly and came towards me, almost upsetting the cart she was pulling. She made a fuss, too, over Raq, whom I had left tied to the gate lest he should go near the sharp blades of the machine.

Tim pulled up the horses when I reached him, and to give him a rest I took the reins and he walked beside me.

My job was an easy one, for Betsy and Fanny were experienced horses and knew their work well. We could not talk much owing to the rattle of the machine, so when I saw a leveret dash out of the grass ahead of us and make for the hedge, I drew Tim's attention to it by pointing to it. The leveret had intended to sneak through the hedge into the oats in the next field, but when it saw us it changed its mind and ran along the ditch with a curious dot-and-carry-one gallop.

" Poor little chap ! It has lost its hiding-place," I said.

Tim then described how he had seen bewildered-looking partridges and pheasants dashing with their chicks out into the open, as the remorseless, noisy cutter went round and round the field, lessening the area of their refuge yard by yard.

The fresh scent of the newly-cut grass was a joy to me, and I was just about to comment on it when suddenly I saw a movement ahead, right in front of the horses. I pulled up sharply. " Look out ! " I called to Tim, just as the brown head of a corncrake appeared above the grass stems to our right. I was off my seat in a moment, and together we searched in the grass in front of the horses.

It was not long before we found a little depression in the ground with the grasses surrounding it arched to form a domed roof. A few more grasses were twisted into a cushion on which lay some buff-coloured eggs, blotched with red markings.

" Ten of them," Tim counted. " Rather like a moor hen's eggs, aren't they ? "

" Yes. They are relations. Coots and rails belong to the same family, too."

We were just discussing what we should do, when Mr. Fletcher came into the field. I left Tim to hold the horses while I went over to him and told him of our discovery.

" I'm not surprised," he said. " Them corncrakes have been keeping the missus awake at night, but she hasn't heard 'em so much lately."

I, too, had often heard their monotonous rasping crakes.

I told him that as soon as the eggs are laid, the cock-corncrake usually becomes less noisy, so this accounted for her not having been disturbed so much lately.

He was very sympathetic when I told him that Tim, and I wanted to save the eggs.

" Oh aye," he said heartily. " I like to hear 'em about. They remind me of when I was a boy. On our farm I used to hear half a dozen of 'em in spring. There aren't many of 'em about nowadays."

I did not like to tell him that I thought the mowing machines were partly responsible for their destruction. When the fields were cut by hand in his youth, nests were more easily avoided.

He then came over and had a look at the nest, and was just in time to see the mother-bird pop her head up farther down the field. " Don't worry, old lady," called Tim. " We're going to save your nest."

Without telling me what he was going to do, Mr. Fletcher went to the side of the hedge and began cutting a pathway around, the nest, so that, when he had finished, it stood in a small island of long grass. He then told me not to continue cutting right round the field, but to cut the grass nearest to the nest. " Cut this top side three or four times," he told Tim, " then the rattle of the mower, won't disturb her, and it'll give her a chance of gettin' back on to her eggs."

Tim was delighted, " I think she'll come back all right, Dad. She stuck it out till Fanny and Betsy were right on top of her."

" Yes; I think that shows that the eggs are about ready for hatching out," I said.

We then cut the top side of the field a few times so that the mower would not frighten her, and after another couple of journeys right round the field, I returned to the vardo, and Tim and Mr. Fletcher went home for dinner.

It was about six o'clock that Tim came racing up the steps to tell me that the corncrake had returned to the nest and was sitting tight. This was very good news.

" Now we'll be able to watch her," he said eagerly.

" Yes; but don't forget she is a ground-nesting bird," I said.

" I see what you mean. The chicks won't stay in the nest. They'll start running around almost as soon as they are hatched."

" And she won't have any grass to hide them in, either,"

I said, and when he looked disappointed, I added," But the comcrake is not quite so bad as the curlew in this respect, so we may see something of them."

That week the weather was ideal for hay making-warm sunshine with a fair breeze, and as the grass lay cut it looked a beautiful green-yellow colour, not the bleached, brittle appearance it has when the sun is too hot and there is no wind. We were therefore soon able to get it into big cocks-always a relief to a farmer, because, once it is in cock, hay can stand out for weeks, even in varied weather, without taking much harm.

This suited Tim and me well, because we had planned to use one of the haycocks as a hide. As a matter of fact, Tim had already begun to build up a special one, not far from where the bird was sitting. We piled the hay up higher on two sides of it to allow for shrinkage, and added a few light branches from the wood near by. On this we piled more grass, and when finished it made a natural grass cave with an entrance at the back of it.

On the second day after we had finished making the cave, Tim came to tell me that all but one of the eggs were hatched out. " Little black fluffy beggars," he said excitedly, " not a bit like their mother."

So that evening we left Raq in the vardo and made our way to the field, keeping behind the hedges as much as possible until we finally crept into the cave. We then made two peep-holes which gave us each a full view of the island.

" She's gone," Tim whispered disappointedly.

" Wait a bit," I said, knowing that the island of grass in which the nest lay was quite a decent size, and that she would hardly have risked taking her none too strong chicks out into the open so soon after hatching. We had waited about half an hour, and even I had begun to think that we were on a hopeless quest, when I noticed a grass stem moving on the far side of the island. " It may be a mouse, or vole, or even a rat," I whispered. After a few more minutes' suspense, the corncrake popped her head above the grass, then disappeared again.

" Keep well under cover, Tim, " I whispered. "If a wood pigeon flies over and sees you, it will give warning and spoil everything." Then, to our delight, the corn- crake appeared on our side of the island, and began to scratch the ground and call her chicks to the food.

" Same way as the young grouse feed," Tim whispered as she picked up some small insects and gave them to the chicks in turn. They managed to move about fairly well, but we noticed that they had not half the strength or stamina of the young curlews and plovers we had watched.

Though the mother was not a beautiful bird, it was easy to see how her chestnut-coloured, wedge-shaped body helped her to thread her way through the long mowing- grass with both ease and speed.

" Where is her mate ? " Tim asked.

I told him that the father rarely put in an appearance until about four days after the chicks had been hatched, and that we might see him later. We did see him a day or two after, flying from the nest to the top of the field, and Tim got much amusement from watching him. He was by no means a good flier and, like a moorhen, he did not seem to know what to do with his long, unwieldy legs.

" Why doesn't he tuck them up behind-like a sea-gull ? " Tim said.

" I don't know. How he manages to fly down to South Africa each winter beats me. He hardly seems to have enough strength even to reach the moor."

One morning when we were waiting in the haycock, Tim nudged my arm. I looked through my peep-hole and saw a pheasant strutting past towards the island where the young chicks were. He had stopped to scratch the ground and pick up something, when to his dismay the cock-corncrake appeared from nowhere and rushed at him like a fury.

He had hardly recovered his wits when the corncrake prepared to rush again. Though the pheasant could have used his spurs to pro- tect himself, he had been so scared by the suddenness of the attack that he ran away to the hedge, completely unnerved.

" That was plucky," Tim said admiringly.

As we were leaving the field, two gun-shots rang out in quick succession. " Jim must be in Bluebell Wood," I said, giving Tim a meaning look. As we turned our footsteps in that direction, we met the gamekeeper just coming out of the wood.

" Look ! He's got the ginger cat ! " Tim cried as he ran ahead.

Though I thought of poor Fan and felt glad that he was now avenged, I could not help feeling sorry for the cat too. He had had to pay a big price for forgetting that he was a domestic animal, and choosing an evil life.

" Was he in that oak tree we told you about ? " Tim asked.

Jim nodded. " He was an' all. I left him a few days to settle down after the scare Raq gave him. I was afraid he might decide to quit his hiding-place, but I was lucky."'

He then described how he had climbed a neighbouring tree and got above him before using his gun.

" Couldn't you have shot up at him from the ground ?" Tim asked.

" Not a pellet would have got through that thick mass of leaves. He would have sat tight and laughed at me."

As I listened to Jim's story, I consoled myself by thinking of the scores of song-birds and game-birds whose lives Jim's act had saved.

Before he left us he turned towards Tim and put his fingers on his lips. Tim replied solemnly with a similar gesture, meaning that he would tell no one how the cat had come to such an untimely end.

" Cats who take to hunting never die-they just disappear," I told Tim. " Their owners would never believe the damage they cause, so it's better to say nothing."

That night I broke the sad news to Tim that I should be going away in a few weeks' time, as I intended taking to the road in my vardo once more. He looked a bit crest- fallen at first, but soon forgot his disappointment when I began to talk about Kek and Fan.

A few nights later Tim was sleeping with me in the vardo when the rain began to patter so violently on the roof that it woke us both up. Ordinarily, he would have been disappointed at such weather, but not so this time.

" No hay making tomorrow, Romany," he said with a knowing wink. " Let's go up to Kestrel Ledge. We shan't see the young hawks again unless we go soon."

Two minutes after I had promised to go he had fallen contentedly to sleep.

The next morning we called at the farm early to make sure that Tim would not be wanted, and Mr. Fletcher agreed that they would not be busy even if the weather improved. When his father asked him why we had got up so early, Tim told him that we had a few jobs to do at the Tan, but he did not mention the kestrels.

Mrs. Fletcher, meanwhile, having heard our conversation from the kitchen, was packing up a parcel of food for us. " He's only young once," she said with a smile.

" What about your mother signalling to us early tomorrow morning if they want you, Tim? " I asked, and I suggested that if they put a lighted lamp in one of the bedroom windows facing the Tan, we should be able to see it when we got up.

" Aye. That'll do," said his father.

With our haversacks full to overflowing we then went on our way, having collected Raq from the stackyard, where he was chasing the farm cats in and out of the various buildings. As there had been heavy rain during the night, I suggested that we should walk along the bank of the river, and then up through Dene Wood on to the moors.

" We'll see what autographs there are," I said.

"Autographs ? " Tim queried, and I explained that the muddy bank and sandy bays should have the footprint signatures of every bird and animal that had visited the stream the previous night.

Tim soon recognised the broad toe-marks of a moor-hen and the smaller ones of her chicks, and as for the small hand-like tracks of rats, we found them everywhere.

It was not long before I came across five-toed pad- marks of an otter, which we followed carefully for some distance. At one time Raq nearly spoilt everything by running ahead and almost obliterating the tracks, and the more we shouted at him the more damage he did by running backwards and forwards. However, we put him on the leash and picked up the otter's tracks farther along the bank. Then I heard Tim shout with delight.

The tracks led up to a large slab of shelving rock, and on it lay a freshly killed sea-trout with one bite eaten out of its shoulder. This in itself was sufficient proof to me that an otter had been at work.

" It looks as though something may have disturbed it just as it was settling down for its meal." This made us search around for further clues. Finally I found the trident-like footprints of a heron on the far side of the rock.

" I shouldn't be at all surprised if he didn't spoil the otter's game. You can tell by the depth of those footprints that the heron stood there, as still as a statue, for a very long time. The otter, having caught the sea-trout, brought it up here to eat it, but just as it was taking the first bite, it caught sight of the heron and shot down into the stream out of reach of its long cruel bill."

Tim nodded from time to time in agreement with my story. " What shall we do with the sea-trout ? " he asked.

" Fetch me a couple of those big rhubarb leaves and we'll take it home for supper." As I lifted it in my bag I guessed that its weight was over two-and-a-half pounds.

Tim chuckled. " A stoat found a supper for us last week and now it's an otter." He then asked why the heron did not eat the sea-trout himself.

" I have never seen him eat anything that was not alive. A heron prefers to catch his fish, frogs, or rats himself. We must thank him, too, because if he hadn't been here there wouldn't have been any fish left for us."

" Rats? " asked Tim.

I nodded. " Yes. They are scared to death of being stabbed by his long bill, so they always keep well out of his way."

Leaving the river, we followed the stream, which narrowed as it reached the rising ground, and came to several small waterfalls surrounded by cool green mosses and ferns. While I watched a pair of kingfishers flying to and fro, Tim lay flat on the bank watching the shoals of minnows in the water below. Catching sight of us, a leader seemed to emerge from their ranks. Dashing ahead of the shoal, he sped up stream at an amazing rate, and they followed like a flock of sheep.

" Useless beggars," Tim remarked. " Sea-trout are good to eat."

" Not useless, Tim. Thousands of them are sent abroad to tropical countries where fever is caused by mosquitoes. They eat the eggs of the mosquito." This was news to Tim, and he at once changed his opinion of the usefulness of minnows.

Meanwhile Raq, bored by our interest in the minnows, had been hunting in the field near by, and to his great delight had put up a hare. She played the usual trick on him and turned and galloped uphill. He might as well have tried to chase an aeroplane, for his speed was no match for hers even on level ground. When he gave up the chase and met us higher up the stream, he was panting and blowing after his efforts, and ready to cool himself by sitting down in the middle of the stream.

" You're tired, old man, aren't you ? " Tim called to him, and I told him not to be too sympathetic, because a dog's only means of perspiration is through its tongue, and that a panting dog is not necessarily an exhausted dog.

Raq then dried himself by rolling in the grass and sliding his nose along through the soft turf.

Higher and higher we followed the stream until the sight of a wheatear and her family told us that we were once more on the moor land. Tim could not resist going to the spot where the crows had feasted on the dead lamb, and when he caught me up he told me that there was nothing to be seen-but a few bones, bleached white by the hot sun.

To save time, he volunteered to go on to the Tan with our haversacks and then follow me along our usual path towards the ravine. Ambling along through the heather, I hoped I might see something of the golden plovers, but I was unlucky. Looking up, however, I saw a buzzard mounting higher and higher into the air. I lay on my back and got out my binoculars and followed its seemingly motionless flight until it became a distant blur. it was lucky that I got up at that moment, because I was just in time to see Tim dashing towards me.

" Gosh ! " he cried, as he jumped clear of me. " I never saw you. "

Making our way up the gully to our hide, we found it very wet after the recent heavy-rains, but otherwise just as we had left it. Tim was the first to climb the tree and inspect Kestrel Ledge. " The young hawks are still there," he whispered.

" We're lucky," I said. " The may leave the nest any day now." As they sat preening themselves we noticed how much they had grown since our last visit. They were now fully feathered, and showed their strength by flapping their wings up and down as , though impatient to use them.

It was amusing to see their surprise when they found themselves lifted off their feet involuntarily and landed on another part of the ledge.

Their restlessness worried us both, because at times they shuffled about so close to the edge of the ledge that we were afraid they would topple over.

One of them seemed more backward than the rest and spent most of his time lying down snapping at the flies that surrounded the evil-smelling nest.

From time to time they peered around anxiously, as though expecting something-Fan's arrival with food, but there was no sign of Fan and we had already been watching them for two hours.

A loud chorus of guttural cries, however, made us glance up the ravine just in time to see her floating down towards the ledge. Instead of throwing the vole to them as before, she alighted on the far corner of the ledge and stood there dangling it in her bill. She seemed to be saying, " Come and fetch it," and as the young hawks shuffled towards her, she kept dropping the vole and then picking it up just as they were about to pounce on it. In fact, she seemed thoroughly impatient with them. No doubt she was thinking that it was time they were venturing out into the world themselves to find their own food, and that she intended to do no more for them.

When they eventually grabbed the vole, they tore it in pieces and swallowed it in huge lumps. Fan stood for a few minutes watching them, and then flew off once more.

Nothing much happened for the next hour or two, and then, to our surprise, it was Kek who returned, bringing the youngsters a young rat. Before they could tear it to pieces he made sure of a slice for himself-a thing we had never seen Fan do. Their behaviour towards him, too, was very different. When they had finished their meal, instead of flapping around him clamouring for more food, they crouched down and glared at him as though they disliked him intensely. He stood there for a while ignoring them. Finally he flew off, and there was something in his joyous flight that made me say to Tim, " He's done with them. I think this is the last time we shall see him here."

And it happened that I was right. He never visited Kestrel Ledge again.

Whilst waiting for Fan we had our lunch, taking it in turns to watch for her return. When she did come, we might have missed her altogether, for instead of alighting on the ledge, she came down on another ledge of rock a yard or two from it. This meant that to get the food she had brought, the youngsters would have to jump or fly across a deep chasm.

" She knows what she is doing," I whispered. " As long as they have their food brought to them, they will never use their wings."

At first they all ventured to the edge of the ledge and stood there uttering piteous cries. Fan had no pity.

" You must fetch it if you want it," she was saying.

Then one of the youngsters flew up on to the huge boulder, half jumped and half flew across the chasm, landing safely. The second one was not so fortunate.

He flapped his wings so violently that he toppled over and we expected to see him crash down into the ravine, but fortunately for him there was a projecting ledge ten yards below. On this he bumped. The cries for food above him, however, made him realise that he was missing his share, so with a frantic effort he flapped his wings, and to his surprise and joy landed on the ledge above.

When the whole family were re-united and, had finished their meal, Fan prepared to leave them.

"' Look, Romany! They are trying to follow her."

Unsteadily, one after another, they launched themselves into the air, landed on the cliff edge a short distance away, and Kestrel Ledge knew them no more.

The following day was not a pleasant one for Tim, for we spent it clearing the Tan of our personal belongings, in readiness for my departure early the following morning.

As I turned the key in the lock and handed it to Tim, I too felt sad when I thought of the many happy hours it had given us.

Mr. and Mrs. Fletcher and Tim all arrived early the next morning, bringing Comma with them, and while I went to say good-bye to Jim and Betty, they harnessed her and put her into the shafts.

As I turned the bend in the lane, I looked back and saw them waving to me, and hoped it would not be long before I saw them all again.

Interior of the Methodist Central Hall, Carlisle.

Interior of Buxton Road Methodist Chapel, Huddersfield.

The Memorial Bird Bath, Old Parks Farm, Glassonby. Where Bram's ashes were scattered.

The Cains erected for Romany and the last Raq in the memorial garden at Wilmslow.

"Gipsy Smith" or Bram's Uncle Rodney, the famous Evangelist. A lifelong mentor and friend.

The Vardo today, after its painstaking restoration. Taken from a Lance Stapley photograph.

ROMANY OF CHILDREN'S HOUR. GOLCAR C. of E. SCHOOL.

JAN. 21st 1939

Above: Sent to the author in 1992.

Left: Romany of the B.B.C. with Raq-the usual, and favourite B.B.C. photograph.

THE FARM

The farm, where Bram's ashes were scattered, played a key role in his books and broadcasts. This is no surprise given a little background information about it. Old Parks is still a working farm, at Glassonby in Cumbria. Bram found it during his time in Carlisle and made friends with the owners. He went there first in 1921, introduced by Arthur Gibson, who was then the County Land Agent for Cumberland.

The Potter family were a traditional Methodist family and so it was no surprise that he got a warm welcome. But he also found a place where his soul could be at peace. The friendship with the Potters lasted twenty two years. The brothers Alan and Joe gave him a wealth of stories to draw upon for his broadcasts and writing, and they were very proud of the fact. They were the family with whom Bram first listened to the radio. It was in September 1923 that he discussed with Joe how "In the years to come... town-dwellers may be able to listen to these beautiful country sounds". Bram always thought that it was strange that it was there on the farm that the idea of broadcasting nature programmes was first mentioned to him; and that the farm would later play so great a part in his life. Tim came from the farm and most of the Romany anecdotes were drawn from local people. After his death Eunice was always welcome there. Much of her biography of Bran was written there, where they had always been so happy.

Bram describes his own feelings best:

"Here I find true peace and solitude. I can roam over eight hundred acres of God's own country without meeting a soul.

Wakened early by the full-throated bird-chorus, I went into the farmyard. To see marvellous sights? Oh, no. Just the ordinary daily round of the farm:- the everlasting flowers of husbandry.

I like the honesty and reticence of speech that marks the countryman - no superlatives, no exaggerations, no striving after effect."

As the farm was such an inspiration, we are lucky that we can still go to see the landscape that so pleased him. If you, reader, are keen enough to find out why exactly he felt as he did then I would urge you to go to Cumbria and just walk. Get out of your car in the country, go for a walk, and as you do so listen to the sounds around you: the birds and animals. The sound that the wind makes as it breathes across the hills. Keep your eyes open. Observe all that is happening. If there is a farmer about, watch what he is doing and ask yourself why. If there is a shepherd working with his dog then stand and see how well they work together: how perfect the understanding between man and animal can be.

When you have seen all of these things think about Romany and what he said, then you too, may understand the Spirit of Romany.

ROMANY'S LEGACY

Everyone that I have spoken to about Romany has wanted to know why someone in their early twenties has become sufficiently interested in a man who died 26 years before his birth to write a book about him. The simple fact that my Father passed on one of his favourite books to me does not really account for the level of enthusiasm that I have felt. I have thought long and hard and have come to the conclusion that there is a magical quality in the way that Bram wrote. Every time I pick up one of his books, within only a few lines I am with him in the fields. He has the power to take people with him and to hold their imagination. I think that he is one of very few writers who were able to transfer their own passion successfully from the spoken word to the page. In giving us 'Romany', someone who was, in essence, a fictitious character , Bram has provided thousands of people with a focus for their interest in the natural world. Bram was ahead of his time in many of his ideas about the countryside and environment. He could be labelled a prototype "Greenie". He recognised that the countryside was changing, often for the worse, and that if people were not careful the effects of these changes would be detrimental. He was never happy to see a tractor ploughing where horses had done the job only a few years before.

His concern was not simply that it was the "old way" to use a pair of horses, but that the tractor's fumes and split oil were polluting the land. He also saw that it now only took one man to plough hundreds of acres where there would once have been a team of up to ten. He realised that the natural world has always operated in a state of balance and equilibrium: from the food chain up to the seasons of the year.

Everything is cyclic and comes around in its turn. If man tries to disrupt this then there will be ecological disaster and a great price to pay. Romany was a great angler and certainly not a vegetarian. He used to shoot game until the mid 1930's and rarely criticised anyone else for it. I am certain that he would have abhorred the current vogue on the "Glorious Twelfth" when foreigners descend on the moors to 'cull' game birds. But he had no complaints about the gamekeeper shooting to keep his birds, as long as it was not indiscriminate. As for fox hunting, I do not see Romany as a hunt saboteur, but I imagine that he felt it very unfair to set a pack of hounds after one fox.

I believe that there is one thing that can be labelled as "The Legacy of Romany". The vast majority of us, whether we are from the town or the country, take at least a passive interest in the natural world. Whether we only watch a programme on television or if we actively go out to seek things for ourselves, in some way we should thank Romany for this. He was the first nationally heard broadcaster who took nature as his theme and was able to show how wide a subject it was and how much there was to see and know. Bram would have been surprised to be called an expert on anything. But he understood the value of learning. His mind was always open, and if we are wise enough we should learn from his example.

After Bram's death Eunice was thrust into the spotlight, but she understood that her husband had been held in very great esteem and that many wanted to say good-bye to him. She agreed to become a member of the committee of the Romany Memorial Fund. This was an organisation that formed to collect money for a 'suitable' memorial. This idea was realised in 1950 when the vardo in its Memorial Garden was opened fully to the public in Wilmslow. The garden was not a formal plot. It was wild, with heather and broom and there was a larch tree, just as there has been at Hardstruggle. The caravan had been used since Romany's death as a focus for his listeners and numerous well wishers. Muriel and Doris were present at the ceremony and accepted donations to the memorial fund. The care and upkeep of the vardo and the Romany memorial walk were handed over to the local council in 1950 together with a sum of money to help with maintenance of the memorials, which included a cairn to Romany and a smaller one in memory of the last Raq.

Eunice lived on until 1977. She played a huge part in Bram's life, and without her he would not have been able to live the life that he did. She built her own life around her husband and ran day to day church business, thus allowing him the time and the opportunity for all of his outside interests. She edited the books, corrected the newspaper articles and although Bram wrote the 'bones' of the radio scripts, it was Eunice who fleshed them out. During the Wilmslow years Bram needed a lot of looking after and she was happy to do this. It was Eunice's own idea to write his biography.

At his father's request Glyn tried to continue the success of the Romany books, but he did not have the same spark and the two that he wrote after his father's death were not as successful. Glyn was an Oxford Graduate and industrial psychologist, employed to decide whether people were suitable for the jobs that they were doing, or if applicants really suited the advertised position. Glyn died in Cambridge in 1978, a year after his mother. He was married twice but left no children. His widow survived him and lives in London.

As for Romany June, she is very much alive and lives in Oxfordshire with her second husband, jazz musician Tommy Watt. Her life and career are in some ways just as fascinating as her fathers. She enlisted in the W.R.N.S. during the 1939-45 war and was a member of the S.O.E. at Bletchley. Her highly secret duties included helping to crack the Enigma code. After the war she went to R.A.D.A., and spent the 1950 season with the Royal Shakespeare Company.

In 1948 she married her first husband, Kenneth Bruce Findlater Bain, better known as theatre critic and historian, Richard Findlater. They had four children, three of whom were triplets. Although this unexpectedly large family put paid to her acting career, she began writing humorously about the problems of brining them up. Within six months she was writing a weekly column for London's "Evening Standard", and spent the next 35 years writing regular features and interviewing stars for most of the major nationals and magazines. In 1962, she married jazz musician Tommy Watt. They had one son, Ben. He is now one half of the popular music duo "Everything But The Girl". Romany's elder children include a successful journalist, an accountant, a personal assistant, and carrying on the Evens tradition, a priest, who is also a clown. Last year the Rev. Rolly Bain published a book about his unusual vocation, entitled "Fools Rush In". Romany June retired in 1990, after spending a decade editing the problem page of the T.V. Times. She worked first on "Dear Katie..." and then on " Dear Miriam" She still contributes articles on travel and nature subjects to The Observer.

During the research for this book I have been surprised at the amount of Romany material that still exists. It is quite possible to travel the country and visit "Romany Related" sites. I have listed them here:

Carlisle. The Central Methodist Hall in Fisher Street stands in the town centre and visitors are welcomed very warmly. The tablet is still in place. Sitting in the "nave" One still feels a great sense of atmosphere and of Bram's presence.

Glassonby. At Old Parks farm there is a memorial bird-bath. On a grassy knoll in a field where sheep graze. It was erected by Bram's friends Mr. and Mrs. Potter. The inscription reads "Sacred to the Memory of the Rev. G. Bramwell Evens (Romany of the B.B.C.) whose ashes were scattered on this place. Born 1884, died 20th November 1943. He loved birds and trees and flowers and the wind on the heath." Visitors to this memorial have to pass through the farm yard. if visiting, please call at the farm house to ask permission. You can take flowers.

Halifax. The King Cross Church is much as it was in Bram's time. The original manse is gone, but

Wainwrights Tower that kept Eunice so much in fear remains. The second house is now in private hands.

Huddersfield. There is nothing physical here to show that the Evens' lived in the town. Their house in Fitzwilliam Street is there, but is again in private hands. The Chapel in Buxton Road was demolished to make way for a new road development in the 1960's.

Wilmslow. This must be the goal for any Romany pilgrim. The vardo has recently been restored by the council in Macclesfield and is open on the first Saturday in the month during the summer. Many friends from the past visit it regularly. Romany June was there a few times in 1993 and 1994 and so was I. Romany's house is still standing and the cairns to him and Raq , are well looked after. The memorial garden has been restored and replanted with some of Bram's favourite plants. One sad note is that the vardo is now fenced in by sturdy iron railings. This is rather incongruous given the nature of the vardo's history, but I understand that it is necessary, unfortunately, because of vandalism suffered in the 1980's.

To coincide with the re-opening the council commissioned a play to be written about Romany's life and this is periodically produced by "Scandalous Productions" and stars Keith Clifford. It is well worth seeing as the production well captures the atmosphere of the broadcasts and lectures that Bram gave. It was one of the focal points of the Wilmslow Arts Festival in the Summer of 1992.

To commemorate the fiftieth anniversary of Bram's death a service was held in the Central Hall in Carlisle. It included a performance of the play and is perhaps best described by Romany's daughter who was there.

I am very grateful to her as I was unable to attend the Anniversary in Carlisle through ill health. I will print her record of the event as it was written for me.

21st November 1993. 2 pm

On the third weekend in November, 1993, a couple of hundred people of all ages gathered in the Central Methodist Church, Fisher Street, Carlisle to commemorate the death of their minister the Rev. G. Bramwell Evens, Romany of the B.B.C., fifty years before. It was a suitable venue as the church was built during his 12 year ministry(1912-1926)and he played a major role designing the interior.

It was opened on April 23rd, 1923. The audience had come to see award winning actor, Keith Clifford, give his one-man show, 'ROMANY - A CELEBRATION', written by John Chambers.

A most striking banner sewn by the ladies of the church stood below the pulpit, emblazoned "Rev. G. Bramwell Evens" and delightfully decorated with birds and animals, his vardo and dog Raq. After the well remembered 'Lullaby of the Leaves' was played on the piano the craggy faced actor staggered in from the vestry wearing a spotted red kerchief and carrying a beer bottle. He began by portraying Bram's grandfather, Cornelius Smith, before he and his brothers were converted.

The years sped by and suddenly Clifford conjured up Romany himself, gentle and humorous, with rough lilting voice, patched jacket and pipe in hand. He spoke of his parents, his childhood, his ministry and his years on Children's Hour. But above all, he spoke of his abiding love of nature, and his fears that the countryside would one day disappear beneath roads and buildings. It was a magical hour's performance and the message was astoundingly topical. A man well ahead of his time was begging us to save our planet."

Before re-reading the selections I have made from the original stories Bram wrote I would like to thank Bram's daughter again and Leslie Horton, John Thorpe and Olive Ambrose for their parts in maintaining Romany's memory, and for helping me so selflessly.

POST SCRIPT

As I completed the draft of this book I was listening to the radio and heard the news that Jack Hargreaves has died from cancer at the age of 82. I immediately through of Hargreave's "Out of Town" series. It must have been the first time in ten years. But as I remembered the Sunday lunch-times spent watching his programmes I suddenly recalled that he was able to instil in me the exact same feelings that Romany's writings always have done. In his "Country Boy" series Hargreaves could easily have been continuing the Romany theme, but on television rather than radio. Tributes paid to Hargreaves echo those paid to Bram, fifty years earlier: "Jack was Britain's greatest broadcaster. He was a natural, a great communicator. He would talk about anything without a script or autocue for as long as anyone wanted without ever being boring."

The B.B.C. said of Bram after his death: "Mr. Evens was regarded as one of the greatest broadcasters who served the B.B.C. He was outstanding not merely because of his wide and curious knowledge of country life and his knack of conveying it vividly "over the air", but because of a microphone technique that seemed to be natural to him. The microphone never cramped him: indeed sometimes when broadcasting he seemed almost to be ignoring it."

I am sure that when they meet in heaven, and their heaven must surely be one of rolling countryside and a spaniel at heel with a perpetually wet nose, they will have much to talk about, and so very much in common.

To add to the sad loss of Jack Hargreaves; Gerald Durrel and James Herriot have both also passed away whilst this book has been in preparation. I can see all three of them sharing a snug corner of heaven with Romany, enjoying a quiet pipe and the sights and sounds of the countryside together.

ROMANY EXTRACTS

When the books were published.

THE ROMANY BOOKS

A Romany in the Fields.

A Romany and Raq.

A Romany in the Country.

A Romany on the Trail.

Out with Romany.

Out with Romany Again.

Out with Romany Once More.

Out with Romany by the Sea.

Out with Romany by Meadow and Stream.

Out with Romany by Moor and Dale.

All of these are by Bram.Published by The Epworth Press or by The University of London Press.

Romany, Muriel and Doris.

Romany Turns Detective.

Romany's Caravan Returns.

A Romany on the Farm.

These were written by Glyn Evens in The Epworth Press or The University of London Press.

The Spirit of Romany.

A St Hugh's Booklet. Compiled by his friend H.L. Gee.

Through the Years with Romany.

The Biography written by Eunice.The University of London Press.